Discovering Mathematics with the TI-73:
Activities for Grades 7 and 8

Edited and revised by

Ellen C. Johnston
Consultant
Fort Smith, AR

Important notice regarding book materials

Texas Instruments makes no warranty, either expressed or implied, including but not limited to any implied warranties of merchantability and fitness for a particular purpose, regarding any programs or book materials and makes such materials available solely on an "as-is" basis. In no event shall Texas Instruments be liable to anyone for special, collateral, incidental, or consequential damages in connection with or arising out of the purchase or use of these materials, and the sole and exclusive liability of Texas Instruments, regardless of the form of action, shall not exceed the purchase price of this book. Moreover, Texas Instruments shall not be liable for any claim of any kind whatsoever against the use of these materials by any other party.

Permission is hereby granted to teachers to reprint or photocopy in classroom, workshop, or seminar quantities the pages or sheets in this work that carry a Texas Instruments copyright notice. These pages are designed to be reproduced by teachers for use in their classes, workshops, or seminars, provided each copy made shows the copyright notice. Such copies may not be sold, and further distribution is expressly prohibited. Except as authorized above, prior written permission must be obtained from Texas Instruments Incorporated to reproduce or transmit this work or portions thereof in any other form or by any other electronic or mechanical means, including any information storage or retrieval system, unless expressly permitted by federal copyright law. Send inquiries to this address:

Texas Instruments Incorporated
7800 Banner Drive, M/S 3918
Dallas, TX 75251

Attention: Manager, Business Services

Chapter illustrations by Jay Garrison Studio.

Coca-Cola, Coke, Sprite, and Mr. Pibb are registered trademarks of the Coca-Cola Company. Pepsi is a trademark of the Pepsi-Cola Company. Dr Pepper is a registered trademark of Dr Pepper/Seven Up Inc. Skittles is a registered trademark of Mars, Inc.

We invite your comments and suggestions about this book. Call us at **1-800-TI-CARES** or send e-mail to **ti-cares@ti.com**. Also, you can call or send e-mail to request information about other current and future publications from Texas Instruments.

Visit the TI World Wide Web home page. The web address is: **http://www.ti.com/calc/**

Contents

Preface

This activity workbook is intended to provide 7th and 8th grade students with an interesting way to explore mathematics. The investigations were designed to spark the curiosity of these students, to make them want to discover the mystery of why, and to motivate them to want to probe into some important mathematical concepts. Most of today's students are "screen literate" and enjoy learning using technology. The activities in this book highlight the functional capabilities of the TI-73 calculator, while making mathematical connections to topics applicable to middle school students.

It was difficult to classify activities into specific strands since another purpose was to make connections between the strands. An attempt to classify according to strand or strands is provided in the **Content and Calculator Functionality Checklist**. Also included in the checklist is a classification of the technology level and some of the calculator functions used. The reason for these categories is to provide the teacher who is new to this technology, information needed to prepare for the lesson. Even though each activity includes detailed keystrokes, the teacher may choose to refer to the TI-73 Guidebook or one of the four appendices in this book.

How to use this Book

Section I: Student Instructions. The first part of each activity contains detailed instructions with keystrokes and screen shots intended for the student or team of students. In most cases one copy would be sufficient for the team doing the investigation. The parts of this section are listed below:

Objective: A brief statement of the activity objective.

Materials: This lets the students know what materials they will need to do the investigation.

Introduction: This section is intended to set the scene for the activity and to spark the students' interest.

In this activity you will: This is the student version of the objectives stated informally.

You will need to know this math vocabulary: This provides the students with vocabulary that they may already be using or may need to learn to use to communicate the mathematics involved in the lesson.

Problem: The statement of the problem to be solved or what the teams are to show in the exploration.

Activity: The specific steps the student or teams of students should go through to do the activity. Directions are included to record information on the Student Worksheet.

Section II: Student Worksheet. This is provided for data collection and analysis. Many of the questions are open-ended. In most cases a copy will be needed for each student.

Section III: Teacher Notes. The information in this section is structured like the student section but goes into more detail. The numbering under *Activity* corresponds to the numbering in the student section. However, some numbers may be left out if there are not any additional teacher tips. Sample data is provided along with some additional teaching and calculator tips. Answers or sample answers are provided for the Student Worksheet.

Section IV: Going Further can be used as an extension or a homework assignment. It may give the teacher ideas for assessment or related assignments.

Each activity can be used as a stand-alone activity and the order presented does not matter. Nonetheless, connections are present in content and concepts that may lend to using the activities in conjunction with each other. Fascinating Fibonacci numbers is a content connection present in Activities 6, 7, and 8. In Activities 3, 4, and 5, students investigate number sense topics of divisibility, GCF, and LCM in a non-traditional context. Experimental and theoretical probabilities are compared in Activities 2 and 11.

Special thanks!

I greatly appreciate the following individuals for their support, ideas, and suggestions:

Jeanie Anirudhan, Nelah McComsey, Karen Pressnell, Karl Peters, and all the other TI folks.

Cathy Cromar, Stephen Davies, Pamela Patton Giles, Gary Hanson, Pamela Weber Harris, Rita Janes, Jane Martain, Linda K. McNay, Melissa Nast, Louise Nutzman, Aletha Paskett, Claudia Schmitt and Karen Wilcox: the development team for *Using the TI-73: A Guide for Teachers*.

Cathy Jahr, Todd Johnson, Linda McNay, and David Young for field testing and reviewing.

The students at Trinity Junior High for their enthusiasm for learning and doing investigations.

And especially my husband Clyde and daughters Adrienne and Emily!

My hope is for this book to aid in helping you motivate your students to want to learn mathematics because after all, Math is FUNctional.

— Ellen Johnston

About the Author

Ellen C. Johnston has worked to motivate students to want to learn mathematics at the middle school/junior high level for the past 12 years in Fort Smith, Arkansas. She sees her role as a motivator more than a teacher. Graphing calculator technology has become an increasingly important tool in her drive to motivate students. Since implementing this tool into her classroom, she has seen students of all abilities "turned on" to mathematics and feels the graphing calculator helps curtail the equity issue allowing all students on the same "playing field." Some of the activities she uses to enrich her 7th and 8th grade classes are included in this book.

At every available opportunity, Ellen promotes Mathcounts (***http://www.mathcounts.org***), which is a national coaching and competition program for 7th and 8th grade students. She serves on the National Coaches advisory council as the Arkansas state liaison and crusades to involve more schools and students in this outstanding program.

Professionally, she is a member of the National Council of Teachers of Mathematics (NCTM) (***http://www.nctm.org***) and has presented at several of the national and regional conferences. Actively involved in the Arkansas Council of Teachers of Mathematics (ACTM), she will serve on the board and as the vice-president of junior high school for the years 1998-2000. In addition, Ellen is an instructor with the Teachers Teaching with Technology (T^3) program (***http://www.ti.com/t3***).

On a personal note, Ellen stays busy as a wife and a mother of two teenage daughters. Her favorite pastime is reading no-brainer novels on the beach because, after all, technology is not allowing her ol' brain much free time.

Content and Calculator Functionality Checklist

Activity	Geometry/ Measurement	Number Sense	Patterns & Functions	Algebraic Reasoning	Probability Statistics	Technology Level	TI-73 Functions Used
Activity 1: Candy Caper		X		X	X	Advanced	list editor, manual fit, text editor, mean, median, mode, box plot
Activity 2: Try Angle?	X			X		Advanced	dice throw, list editor, categorical list, pie chart, stacked fractions
Activity 3: A Prime Investigation		X		X		Beginner	Integer divide, same line display
Activity 4: Oliver's Method		X				Beginner	stacked fractions, same line display, GCD, LCM
Activity 5: It's Greek to Me		X				Beginner	Integer divide, same line display, GCD, LCM
Activity 6: Class of Gold			X	X		Intermediate	lists, conversion, scatterplot, manual fit
Activity 7: Go For the Gold	X	X	X			Beginner	named lists, rounding Mode
Activity 8: Let's Do Summagic		X		X		Intermediate	list editor, sum list, same line display
Activity 9: Taste Test					X	Intermediate	list editor, pictographs, single/triple bar graphs, pie charts
Activity 10: Step Up	X		X	X		Advanced	Draw, store and recall pic, manual fit, Y= editor, conversion
Activity 11: Probably Not					X	Intermediate	coin toss, lists, fractions, double bar graph
Activity 12: A Penny Saved			X	X		Beginner	constant key, lists, scatterplot

Activity 1

The Candy Caper

Objective

♦ To use estimation to determine the number of candies in various size cylinders. You will compare the estimated numbers to the actual numbers and investigate the relationship between the two numbers.

Materials

♦ TI-73 calculator

♦ Student Worksheet

In this activity you will:

♦ estimate the number of candies in each container

♦ find measures of central tendency, the mean, median and mode

♦ compare your estimate with the actual number and investigate the relationship

You will need to know this math vocabulary:

♦ absolute value

♦ mean

♦ median

♦ mode

♦ box-and-whiskers plot or box plot

♦ scatterplot

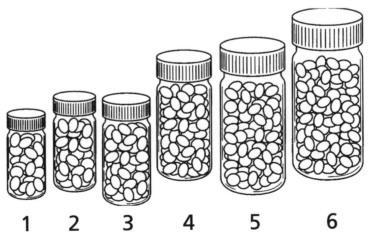

1   2   3   4   5   6

Introduction

You are probably familiar with Skittles™ candy. A pharmacist would probably be a good estimator of how many Skittles™ candies a medicine vial could hold, since pharmacists deal with filling different sized containers with pills of various sizes all the time in their occupation. How good are you at estimating the number of Skittles™ different-sized medicine vials can hold?

Problem

In this activity, you will estimate the number of candies contained in each vial. Record your estimates on the table on the Student Worksheet.

Your teacher will give your team a vial of candies. Find the actual number of candies in the vial. Divide the candy between the members in your group. Sort in groups of 10. Count the candies and tell your teacher this number. After all bottles have been counted, record the actual numbers on the table on the Student Worksheet.

Activity

1. The List editor ([LIST]) will be very helpful in determining how well you estimated. Before using the List editor, go to the Home screen and execute the SetUp Editor by pressing [2nd] [CATALOG], selecting **SetUpEditor**, and pressing [ENTER] [ENTER].

    a. Enter your estimates in a list named **GUESS** and the actual numbers in a list named **EXACT**.

    ✎ Answer Question 1 on the Student Worksheet.

    b. To find the difference in the two lists, highlight L1 and press [2nd] [STAT]. Select **GUESS** and press [ENTER], then press [−] [2nd] [STAT] **EXACT** [ENTER].

    ✎ Record this data in the fourth column of the table on the Student Worksheet. Answer question 2 on the Student Worksheet.

    c. **Absolute value** is the positive number that you were off on each estimate. To obtain the absolute value of L1 and store in L2, highlight L2, press [2nd][CATALOG], select **abs(** [ENTER], then press [2nd] [STAT] L1 [ENTER][)] [ENTER]. Scroll down L2. These numbers are the positive difference of your guess and the exact number, or how many you were off. Calculate the **mean** of L2 to determine the average number by which you were off. To do this, go to the Home screen and press [2nd] [STAT] [▶] [▶] **MATH**, then select **mean(** [2nd] [STAT] L2 [ENTER] [)] [ENTER].

    ✎ Answer question 3 on the Student Worksheet and copy the data from L2 in the calculator into the fifth column of the table on the Student Worksheet.

    d. Find the percentage you were off on each estimate and put this in L3. To do this, highlight L3 and use the formula L2 [÷] **LEXACT** [×] 100. Then find the mean of L3.

✎ Answer question 4 on the Student Worksheet.

2. Tell your teacher the average number of "candies off" you were. (This was the answer to question 3 on the Student Worksheet.) You will enter the averages of your class members in **L4** on the calculator. Listen as your teacher calls out the numbers and explains how to do this.

    a. Go to the Home screen and sort **L4** in ascending order by pressing [2nd] [STAT] [▶] **OPS**, selecting **1: SortA(** [ENTER], and pressing [2nd] [STAT] **L4** [ENTER] [)] [ENTER]. Press [LIST] and scroll down **L4** to see the averages in order.

✎ Answer question 5 on the Student Worksheet.

    b. Find the mean of the class' "candies off." Press [2nd] [STAT], press [▶] [▶] to move to **MATH**, then select **3:mean(** [ENTER] [2nd] [STAT] **L4** [ENTER] [)] [ENTER].

    c. Find two other measures of central tendency: the **median** and **mode**. Press [2nd] [STAT] [▶] [▶] **MATH**, select **4:median(** [ENTER] [2nd] [STAT] select **L4** [ENTER] [)] [ENTER]. You may follow the same procedure to find the mode, but select **5:mode(** from the **Math** menu. If there is no mode, the calculator will display **ERR:NO MODE**. Select the **Quit** option.

✎ Record these results in question 6 on the Student Worksheet.

3. Set up a statistics plot and create a **box-and-whiskers plot**.

    a. Before doing so, make sure equations are turned off or cleared out of the [Y=] editor. Press [2nd] [PLOT] **4:PlotsOff** [ENTER], [2nd] [PLOT] **1:Plot 1** [ENTER].
Change settings to match those shown at the right. Use [▶] and [▼] to move to the box-and-whiskers symbol, then press [ENTER] to select it. Select **Xlist** by pressing [2nd] [STAT] and selecting **4:L4**.

    b. Set the window by pressing [ZOOM] **7:ZoomStat**. Press [TRACE].

✎ Answer question 7 on the Student Worksheet.

4. Compare your estimated numbers to the actual numbers using a **scatterplot**. When data is displayed in a scatterplot, usually the purpose is to determine if there is an association between the two variables on the graph. If the points seem to fall on or close to a line then there is a relationship. If the points are all scattered out then there is no relationship.

    a. Turn plots off by pressing [2nd] [PLOT] **4:PlotsOff** [ENTER]. Set up plot 1 by pressing [2nd] [PLOT] **2:Plot 1** [ENTER] and entering the settings shown at the right.

b. Press WINDOW and set an appropriate first quadrant window, as shown at the right.

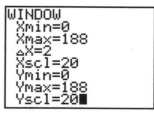

✎ Answer question 8 on the Student Worksheet.

c. Press GRAPH TRACE.

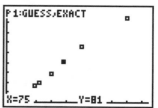

5. You can use **Manual-Fit** to best fit a line on the plotted data. Press MODE and set as shown at the right to round the values to the nearest whole number.

a. On the Home screen, press 2nd [STAT] ◄ **CALC 3:Manual-Fit**, then 2nd [VARS] **2:Y-Vars 1:Y1** ENTER. Position the cursor at the beginning of the line segment that you want to draw, and press ENTER. As you press the cursor keys, the line is drawn and the slope or steepness is adjusted. When you have matched the plotted points as desired, press ENTER. You can use the cursor keys to adjust the line. When you find the best fit, press ENTER again.

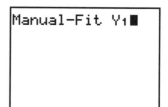

b. The equation of this line has now been pasted in the Y= editor. This is an approximate equation that describes the relationship between your estimates and the actual numbers. What would the relationship be between **X** and **Y** if you had guessed the exact amounts in every container?

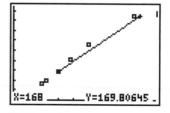

✎ Answer question 9 on the Student Worksheet.

c. Press Y= and turn **Y1** off by highlighting the = sign and pressing ENTER. In **Y2**, type **X** (to create the equation **Y=X**) and press GRAPH.

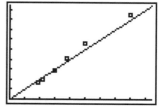

6. The students with the "lowest number of candies off" average and the "highest number of candies off" average will show their scatterplots to the class.

✎ Answer questions 10 and 11 on the Student Worksheet.

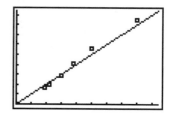

Name _____

Date _____

Activity 1

The Candy Caper

Record your results on the table below. Then answer the questions about the activity.

Part 1 - One-Variable Statistics

Vial #	Estimate LGUESS	Actual LEXACT	L1=LGUESS ⊟ LEXACT	L2=abs(L1)	% off L3=L2 ⊡ LEXACT ⊠ 100
1					
2					
3					
4					
5					
6					
7					
8					
9					
10					

1. How can you determine how close you guessed to the actual number?

   _____

2. Suppose you guessed 30 candies but there were only 25; you were _____ over. On a second vial, you guessed 50 but there were 59, so you were _____ under. How could you find the your average error in this situation?

   _____

   _____

3. The mean number I was off is _____. This means on average I was off _____ candies per bottle. Explain how you find this average without a calculator.

   _____

4. The mean percent I was off was _____. Relate this to your estimate.

_____

_____

_____

5. List all class members' averages in order from least to greatest.

_____

_____

_____

_____

_____

6. The median of the data set in #5 is _____.

The mean is _____.

The mode is _____.

7. Box Plots can often be described as evenly distributed, positively skewed or negatively skewed. Which description best describes the data in the class' box plot? Explain.

_____

_____

_____

_____

Sketch the box plot on this screen.

Part 2 - Two-Variable Statistics

8. Describe the data points on the scatterplot.

    _____

    _____

    _____

    Sketch the plot on this screen.

9. Write an equation to describe the relationship between the estimate (**X**) and the exact number (**Y**) if you had guessed the exact amounts in every container.

    _____

    How does this equation compare to the manual-fit equation?

    _____

10. How does the scatterplot of the person whose mean average was the "lowest number of candies off" compare to the line **Y=X**?

    _____

    _____

    _____

    _____

11. How does the scatterplot of the person whose mean average was the "greatest number of candies off" compare to the line **Y=X**?

    _____

    _____

    _____

Teacher Notes

Activity 1

The Candy Caper

Materials

♦ TI-73 calculator for each student

♦ Student Worksheets (page 5)

♦ ViewScreen

♦ 6 to 10 clean medicine vials of different sizes, labeled with numbers. (A local pharmacy would probably be willing to donate these.)

♦ 1 to 2 large bags of candies (Skittles™ candies work well) or beans

♦ Wet wipes for students to clean their hands (or give them an opportunity to wash their hands, since they will be touching the candy).

Students will use estimation to determine the number of candies in various size cylinders. They will compare their estimated numbers to the actual numbers and investigate the relationship between the two numbers. One- and two-variable statistics will be analyzed.

Vocabulary

absolute value	The number of units the number is from zero on the number line.
mean	The sum of the elements in the set, divided by the number of elements in the set.
median	The middle number of a set of data when the numbers are arranged in numerical order.
mode	The number that occurs the most often in a set of data.

(Vocabulary continued on the next page)

| box-and-whisker plot (box plot) | A graph that shows the minimum value, lower quartile, median, upper quartile and maximum value. It graphically displays the quartiles using the 5 values above as boundary points. If the segments that join the minimum value to lower quartile, lower quartile to median, median to upper quartile, and upper quartile to maximum value are about the same length then the data set is evenly dispersed. If the right whisker is shorter than the left whisker the data is positively skewed. If the left whisker is shorter than the right then the data is negatively skewed. |

Classroom Management

The activity is divided into two parts. Part 1 investigates one-variable statistical topics such as the mean, median and mode and concludes with the analysis of a box plot. Part 2 compares the students' estimate to the actual number using a scatterplot, manual fit, and the [Y=] editor. You may need to divide the activity into two days depending on length of class and ability of students.

Problem

Display the vials of candy on a table in numerical order. Have the students bring a pencil and Student Worksheet and walk by the vials of candy in a single file line, writing down their estimates as they inspect the vials. Do not permit them to touch or pick up the vials. Monitor the line so that each student gets approximately the same amount of inspection time.

Send the students back to their groups, where they will work together to complete most of the activity. Some of the activity will be class-oriented and teacher-directed or the whole activity could be teacher-led. Give each group a vial to count and find the actual number. Tell the students to sort the candy in groups of 10. They may not eat the candy until given permission to do so. Have a member from each group come up to the board and record the exact number of candies contained in their vial. Have the students record this number on the table on the Student Worksheet.

Activity

1. To access lists, name lists, and use formulas in lists, see Appendix A, B, and C, respectively. Sample screen shots are shown below.

L6	GUESS	EXACT	2
▬▬▬	38	34	
	44	40	
	60	59	
	75	81	
	100	113	
	160	171	
	------	------	

L6(1)=

EXACT	◤1	L2	5
34	------	------	
40			
59			
81			
113			
171			

L1 = LGUESS− LEXACT

GUESS	EXACT	L1	3
38	34	4	
44	40	4	
60	59	1	
75	81	-6	
100	113	-13	
160	171	-11	

GUESS(1)=38

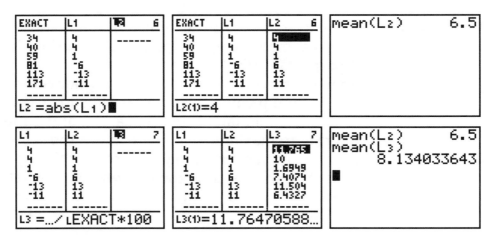

2. This part of the activity will involve the whole class and will be directed by you. Go around the class and have the students tell you their "average off." Enter the data in L4 on a calculator with a ViewScreen display, and have the students enter these numbers in L4 on their calculators. The rest of number 2 can be directed by you, or the students may work in groups. Sample screen shots are shown below. A prize may be given to the student who did the best job estimating if they can verify their estimates. In the second screenshot below, 1.75 was the best estimator.

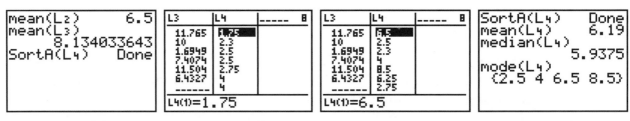

3. For more information about setting up statistical plots see Appendix D. If the students are experienced in setting up plots and are familiar with box-and-whisker plots, they may work through this part of the activity with their group. Otherwise, you may lead them through this part of the activity.

4. If the students are experienced in setting up scatterplots, they may work through this part of the activity with their group. If you lead them through you will need to use a student's data as a sample.

5. You may choose whether to lead them through the manual fit and analysis of data or not depending on your students level and calculator experience. Have the groups with the highest and lowest "number of candies off" display their scatterplots so they can be compared. The lists could be sent to a calculator and displayed on a ViewScreen. (See Appendix E for more information on linking.) One of the lists named **Guess** would have to be renamed so both groups' **Guess** lists could be used. In the [Y=] editor, graph the equation **Y=X** and in plot 1 display the "worst" estimators scatterplot and in plot 2 display the "best" estimators scatterplot. Use a different mark in plot 2.

Answers to Student Worksheet

1. Find the difference in the number you guessed and the exact number

2. You would just look at the positive values. Add 5 and 9 and then divide by 2.

3. Answers will vary. Add the numbers in **L2** and divide by the number of numbers.

4. Answers will vary. (On average, my guess was ___ percent too high or too low.)

5. Answers will vary but should be the same for the entire class. Make sure the data is in ascending order

6. Answers will vary, but should be the same for the entire class.

7. Answers will vary. See **box plot** in vocabulary for a description.

8. Answers will vary. The better the estimates, the more linear the scatterplot will be.

9. **Y=X**. Answers will vary.

10. Answers will vary. The closer the points are to the line, the better the guess.

11. Answers will vary. These points will be scattered more and not as linear.

Going Further

You can make a variation of this activity by estimating ages of famous or well-known people, investigating the relationship between a guess and the person's actual age. To do this, simply make up a list of 10 to 20 people of various ages and find out their actual ages. Good sources are newspapers, magazines, or the Internet. This is a fun and interesting activity to do with parents and children on Family Math Nights.

Activity 2

TryAngle?

Objective

◆ To investigate properties of triangles and learn how to classify the various types of triangles

Materials

◆ TI-73 calculator

◆ 12 6-inch straws with about 40 twist ties

◆ Ruler, scissors, and marker

◆ Student Worksheet

In this activity you will:

◆ discover a test to determine if three line segments can form a triangle

◆ discover a method to classify triangles as acute, right, or obtuse when the side lengths are known

◆ find all possible triangles that can be made

You will need to know this math vocabulary:

◆ scalene, isosceles and equilateral triangles

◆ acute, right and obtuse triangles

Introduction

Adrienne has decided to make a mobile of triangles for a geometry project. She will use straws from 1 to 6 inches (whole number lengths only) for the sides and twist ties to connect them. Can she randomly pick straws and make a triangle? If she wants her mobile to include all possible triangles, how many triangles will she need to make?

Problem

You will work with a partner to obtain all possible triangles by randomly generating three whole numbers between 1 and 6. Three dice will be rolled to determine the side lengths using the TI-73 dice throw function. You and your partner will take turns throwing the dice.

Activity

1. Go to the Home screen [2nd] [QUIT] and press [CLEAR].
    Next press [MATH] [▶] [▶] **PRB** and select **7: dice(**. Type **3**
    [)] to roll three dice as shown at the right. Press
    [ENTER] several times to see the random numbers
    that will come up on the three dice. [CLEAR] your
    screen to start the game.

    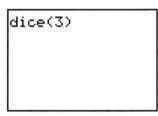

    a. Press [ENTER] and determine who has the highest
        sum. This person will go first. Player 1 will
        press [ENTER] and will try to build a triangle with
        the numbers rolled on the dice as given side
        lengths.

        Use the ruler and cut straws of the given lengths. Insert the twist ties
        in the ends of the cut pieces and try to connect to form a triangle. If
        Player 1 is able to make a triangle with the given lengths, then Player
        2 will inspect it and make sure the sides are measured accurately.
        Player 1 will record his/her results in Table 1. Player 2 will now take a
        turn. For example, if a player rolls the dice 1, 1, 2 and it is determined
        that it is not possible to make a triangle, then the result is recorded as
        1, 1, 2 in the appropriate player column for "not a triangle." Likewise,
        if a player rolls the numbers 3, 4, 5 and it is determined possible to
        make a triangle then these results are recorded in the appropriate
        player column for "is a triangle."

    b. If on a later roll a player rolls 4, 3, 5 when 3, 4, 5 has been rolled
        earlier, it will still count as "is a triangle." The triangle does not need
        to be built again since it would be the same triangle.

    c. To determine a game winner, find the sum of the columns and then
        subtract the "not a triangle" column sum from the "is a triangle"
        column sum. This will become the player's score. The person with the
        highest score is the winner.

    ✎ Answer questions 1 through 3 on the Student Worksheet.

2. One way to classify triangles is by their sides. If all sides are congruent
    (or equal in measure) the triangle is **equilateral**. If two sides are congruent,
    the triangle is **isosceles**, and if no two sides are congruent, then the
    triangle is **scalene**.

    ✎ In Table 1 on the Student Worksheet, write an **E** next to any
    equilateral triangles, an **I** next to any isosceles triangles, and a **S**
    next to any scalene triangles.

3. Another way to classify triangles is by their angle measures. You may recall that the sum of the angles in any triangle is 180°. A **right triangle** has one right angle (90°) and two acute angles. (An acute angle is less than 90°.) An **acute triangle** has three acute angles and an **obtuse triangle** has one obtuse angle and two acute angles. (An obtuse angle measures greater than 90° and less than 180°.) Inspect the triangles you and your partner have made and classify them according to their angles.

✎ In Table 1, write an **R** next to any right triangles, an **A** next to any acute triangles, and a **O** next to any obtuse triangles. Answer questions 4 and 5 on the Student Worksheet.

4. In a right triangle, the square of the hypotenuse (longest side) is equal to the sum of the squares of the other two sides. This important theorem is called **the Pythagorean Theorem**. A set of numbers that satisfy this equation $a^2 + b^2 = c^2$ is called a Pythagorean triple.

a. Test 3, 4, 5 in this equation to see if it is a Pythagorean triple. Press 2nd[TEXT] 3 STO▶ A, select **Done** and press ENTER. Press 2nd [CATALOG] ▲ ▲ ▲(to select :), ENTER. Press 2nd [TEXT] 4 STO▶ B then select **Done** ENTER 2nd [CATALOG] ▲ ▲ ▲ (to select :) ENTER. Finally, press 2nd[TEXT] 5 STO▶ C, select **Done**, ENTER ENTER. Type in the equation and make sure both sides are equal.

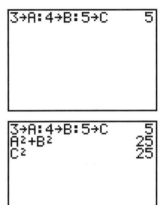

b. Since $3^2 + 4^2 = 5^2$, a triangle with sides of 3, 4, and 5 would be a right triangle. If you do not have a 3, 4, 5 triangle made, make one.

✎ Answer question 6 on the Student Worksheet.

5. Find an acute triangle. If you don't have one already made, make one.

✎ Answer questions 7 and 8 on the Student Worksheet.

6. Use an obtuse triangle you have made. If you don't have one, make three.

✎ Answer questions 9 and 10 on the Student Worksheet.

7. The class will now combine all their data and include any possible missing sets to make an organized list with all possible triangles to be included in the mobile. Remember that 3, 4, 5 is the same as a 5, 3, 4, so don't list twice in the table.

✎ Complete the table with your class and answer question 11 on the Student Worksheet.

Activity 2

TryAngle?

Record your results on the table below. Then answer the questions about the activity.

Part 1

Trial	Player 1: Is not a triangle	Is a triangle	Player 2: Is not a triangle	Is a triangle
1				
2				
3				
4				
5				
6				
7				
8				
9				
10				
Totals				
	Player 1 score:		Player 2 score:	

1. What conclusions can you draw about the lengths of sides of triangles?

   _____

2. Give an example of a set of 3 numbers (different from those in the table above) that could be the sides of a triangle.

   _____

3. Give 3 examples of sets of 3 numbers (different from those above) that could not be the sides of a triangle.

    _____

    _____

4. Why can't a right triangle have two right angles?

    _____

5. An equilateral triangle is said to also be equiangular. What is the measure of each angle in an equilateral triangle?

    _____

6. Does the 3, 4, 5 triangle appear to have one right angle and two acute angles?

    _____

7. Using an acute triangle, let c=_____(the longest side) and let a = _____(the shortest side) and let b=____(the middle side). Replace the $\square$ with <, >, or = to make a true sentence.

    $a^2 + b^2 \ \square \ c^2$

8. Try 2 other triangles that appear to be acute by substituting in the side lengths into the mathematical sentence in #7 and using the correct symbol. (c= the longest side, a and b will be the shorter sides and it is possible for a=b) Make them if you don't have them.

    _____

9. Using an obtuse triangle, let c= (the longest side) and let a = (the shortest side) and let b= (the middle side). It's okay if a=b. Substitute into

    $a^2 + b^2 \ \square \ c^2$

    replacing $\square$ with <, >, or = to make three true sentences.

    _____

10. Compare your results in #7 through #9 above and make a conjecture from your experiment.

    _____

Part 2 - Class Data Table

All triangles with side(s)	List triangles	Total
of 1 inch		
of 2 inches		
of 3 inches		
of 4 inches		
of 5 inches		
of 6 inches		

11. How many triangles would Adrienne need to make for her mobile?

_____

Teacher Notes

Activity 2

TryAngle?

Math Strand

♦ Algebraic reasoning

♦ Number sense

♦ Statistics

Materials

♦ TI-73 calculators (one per pair or for each student)

♦ Student Worksheets (page 16)

♦ 12 six-inch straws for each pair of students

♦ 40 to 50 twist ties for each pair of students

♦ A pair of scissors, a marker, and a ruler for each pair of students

Students will investigate properties of triangles by randomly generating possible side lengths for triangles. They will experimentally try to make triangles with the randomly generated numbers and then make conjectures about triangle inequalities.

Vocabulary

equilateral triangle	A triangle with all 3 sides congruent.
isosceles triangle	A triangle with 2 sides congruent.
scalene triangle	A triangle with no 2 sides congruent.
acute triangle	A triangle with 3 acute angles.
right triangle	A triangle with 1 right angle and 2 acute angles.
obtuse triangle	A triangle with 1 obtuse angle and 2 acute angles.

Classroom Management

Students will work with a partner in the investigation part (Part 1) of the activity.

♦ Demonstrate how to make a triangle with the given materials. Emphasize to the students to measure accurately and use a marker to mark the cut line. Insert the twist ties inside the straws so the straws meet to form vertices. You may need to settle any disagreements students may have on if it is a triangle or not.

In Part 2 of the activity you will lead the class to summarize the data, and the Class Data Table will be completed. The last part is the **Going Further** section and is optional. It could be investigated by the whole class or as a home assignment.

Activity

Part 1

1. If the students are not familiar with the random number generators on the calculator, show them the various ways to generate random numbers. Allowing them to play with the coin toss (for any number of coins) and the dice roll (for any number of dice) will help seed the calculators in case these functions have not been used yet. This will avoid the problem of the calculators generating the same numbers.

   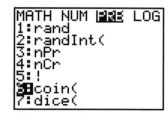

   Press [MATH] [▶][▶] **6:coin(2 [)]** (tosses 2 coins) pressing [ENTER] any number of times. Explain that the numbers **0** and **1** would have to be defined to mean head or tail.

   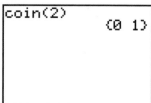

   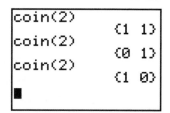

   Do the same with the dice roll, changing the number of dice and discussing what it means.

   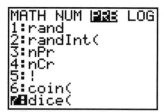

   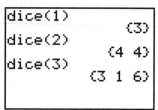

2. Students should have had some prior experience with triangles and classifying by sides.

3. Students should be familiar with angle measure and be able to classify angles as acute, right, or obtuse.

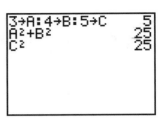

4. You may want to tell the students that after they enter the stored values for **a**, **b**, and **c** and **the Pythagorean Theorem** equation into the calculator once, they don't have to enter it again. They can scroll up, grab and edit if necessary to use again. See screen shots at the right.

5. You may want to re-emphasize that an acute triangle has 3 acute angles.

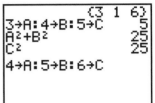

6. You may want to ask students why an obtuse triangle has only one obtuse angle.

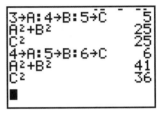

Part 2

7. When completing the Class Data Table, include missing sets. You may start by asking students to tell the sets that have a 1" side. Write this set down in the second column, second row as 111. Next ask the students to tell all their sets that have a 2" side. Write these sets on board as 3-digit numbers, then go back and order them in ascending order. When you get to the 3" sides, tell students that we can not re-use triangles with 2" sides. Suggest starting with the equilateral triangle 333. You cannot go back to 332 (since it was used in the 2" row) so check out 334, 335, 336, 344, 345, 346, 355, 356, and 366. Continue this same process for 4", 5" and 6".

a. In the final part of this activity, use the calculator list to list all 28 triangles and test to make sure they are triangles using the triangle inequality rule discovered. Name the lists **A**, **B**, and **C** to represent the sides. To access, name, and use formulas in lists, see Appendix A, B, and C respectively.

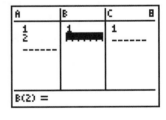

Enter the data going from left to right to reflect the sides of the possible triangles. (It will take longer to enter this way but will probably make more sense to the students.) More experienced students may be able to enter in columns. See the screen shots at the right.

b. Now find the sum of **A** and **B**, scroll down the list and make sure **A + B > C**. Go to the right of **C**. Name the list **SUMAB**. Use the formula **A + B** and then scroll down the list and have students verify that **A + B > C**.

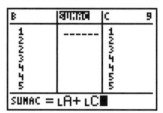

c. To test the second condition of **A + C > B**, insert a list named **SUMAC** to the right of **B** and use the formula **A + C**. Scroll down **SUMAC** list and make sure **A + C > B**.

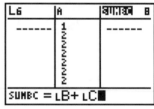

d. Finally, test the third condition of **B + C > A**. Name a list **SUMBC** and insert it to the right of **A**. Scroll down list **SUMBC** and make sure **B + C > A**.

e. Ask students how you can make sure you did not leave any data out. (Make sure the list is organized.) Students can now make a class mobile with all 28 triangles.

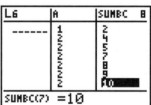

Answers to Student Worksheet

1. The sum of two sides has to be greater than the third side.

2. Answers will vary with lots of possibilities such as {3,4,5} {6,6,5}.

3. Answers will vary with even more possibilities such as {1,2,4} {3,2,6}.

4. The sum of 2 angles would equal 180°, meaning the third angle would be 0°.

5. 60°

6. It should.

7. Sample answer a=4 b=5 c=6 $4^2 + 5^2 > 6^2$

8. Answers will vary. $5^2 + 5^2 > 6^2$ $3^2 + 3^2 > 4^2$

9. Answers will vary. $3^2 + 4^2 < 6^2$, $2^2 + 3^2 < 4^2, 2^2 + 2^2 < 4^2$

10. If $a^2 + b^2 = c^2$, then the triangle is right. If $a^2 + b^2 > c^2$, then the triangle is acute. If $a^2 + b^2 < c^2$, then the triangle is obtuse.

Class Data Table

All triangles with side(s)	List triangles								Total
of 1 inch	111 E-A								1
of 2 inches	222 E-A	223 I-O	234 S-O	244 I-A	245 S-O	255 I-A	256 S-O	266 I-A	8
of 3 inches	333 366 E-A	334 I-A	335 I-O	344 I-A	345 S-R	346 S-O	355 I-A	356 S-O I-A	9
of 4 inches	444 E-A	445 I-A	446 I-O	455 I-A	456 S-A	466 I-A			6
of 5 inches	555 E-A	556 I-A	566 I-A						3
of 6 inches	666 E-A								1

11. 28

Going Further

Students could classify all 28 triangles in the Class Data Table by their sides and angles using **E**-Equilateral, **I**- Isosceles, **S**-Scalene and **A**-Acute, **R**-Right, **O**-Obtuse, as done above. Pie charts could be used to compare the number of specific triangles to the whole.

Triangle by sides	Frequency	Triangle by angles	Frequency
Equilateral	6	Acute	19
Isosceles	15	Right	1
Scalene	7	Obtuse	8
Total	28	Total	28

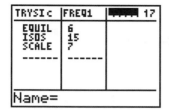

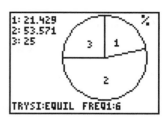

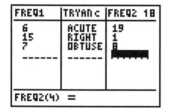

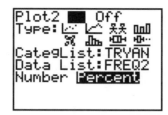

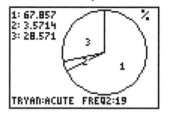

Many different probability questions could be posed, such as:

1. What is the probability of rolling 3 dice and getting a set of numbers that would be a triangle? There are 6^3 or 216 different outcomes. Even though there are 28 triangles, there are more than 28 possible outcomes. For example 345, 354, 435, 453, 534, 543 would be considered one triangle but 6 different outcomes. So if you count the permutations all scalene triangles would have 6 arrangements, Isosceles would have 3, and Equilateral triangles would have only 1 arrangement. Go back to List and multiply the number of equilateral triangles by 1, the number of Isosceles triangles by 3 and the number of Scalene triangles by 6. Sum the List and put that over the total number of possibilities.

    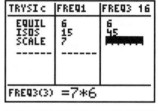

    Students could each roll dice 72 times and see how many would make triangles.

    Compare this experimental probability to the theoretical probability of 31/72.

2. Are you more likely to roll number sets that would or would not make a triangle?

3. How many of your trials in the game produced triangles?

4. What kind of triangle are you most likely to roll?

EXPLORATIONS

Activity 3

A Prime Investigation
with 7, 11, and 13

Objective

♦ To investigate the divisibility of 7, 11, and 13, and discover the divisibility characteristics of certain six-digit numbers

Materials

♦ TI-73 calculator
♦ Student Worksheet

In this activity you will:

♦ investigate the divisibility of 7, 11, and 13

♦ discover why special six-digit numbers are divisible by 7, 11, and 13

You will need to know this math vocabulary:

♦ divisible

♦ factors

♦ distributive property

Introduction

Mathematics can sometimes seem mysterious, sort of like the magic tricks a magician performs. Does the magician know why the tricks work? There are underlying reasons in the mystery of mathematics that explain why it works.

Problem

Choose any three-digit number. Then repeat those three digits in the same order to make a six-digit number, for example 459,459. (Do not use this number.) Write your original number down. Make sure no one in your group has the same number.

Your number is _____.

Activity

Part 1 - The Investigation

1. Find out if your number is **divisible** by 7. It is divisible by 7 if you divide it by 7 and get a remainder of 0. Use integer divide on the calculator to find out.
    Press **459459** [2nd] [INT÷] **7** [ENTER].

    Is your number divisible by 7?

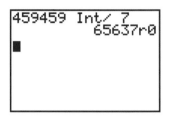

2. Find out if your previous quotient is divisible by 11. Press [2nd] [INT÷] **11** [ENTER].

    Is your number divisible by 11?

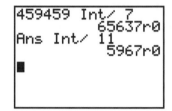

3. Integer divide the previous quotient by 13.

    Is your number divisible by 13? What do you notice about the new quotient?

    ✎ Answer the questions on Part 1 of the Student Worksheet.

Part 2 - Justify why these numbers are divisible by 7, 11, and 13

1. Pick another three-digit number and enter it into your calculator. Repeat the same three digits to form a six-digit number. Test it for divisibility by 7, 11, and 13.

    ✎ Answer question 6 on the Student Worksheet.

2. Multiply 7 x 11 x 13.

3. Divide your number in #1 by the product in #2.

4. Multiply your three-digit number in **#1** by the product in **#2**. What answer did you get?

    ✎ Answer question 7 on the Student Worksheet.

5. Examine the screen shot at the right. Multiplying by 1000 is easy to do mentally because you just move the decimal point 3 places right. Multiplying by 1001 is also easy when you think of 1001 as 1000 + 1 and then multiply 459 x 1000 and add 459 x 1. This is known as the **distributive property.**

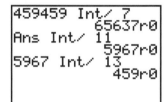

    ✎ Answer questions 8 through 10 on the Student Worksheet.

Part 3 - Divisibility Tests

1. You are probably familiar with the divisibility tests for prime numbers 2, 3, and 5.

    ✎ Write the divisibility tests for 2, 3, and 5 in question 11 on the Student Worksheet.

2. There is also a divisibility test to tell if a number is divisible by 7, but it is somewhat tedious to use on large numbers. Here is how the test works:

    a. Take all but the last digit (units digit) and form a number.

    b. Subtract twice the units digit from the number you formed. Now you have a new number.

    c. Again, take all but the units digit and form a newer number.

    d. Subtract twice the units digit from this number.

    e. Continue this process until you are able to recognize whether the number is divisible by 7. See the screen shown at the right.

    ```
    459459          459459
    45945-18         45927
    4592-14           4578
    457-16             441
    44-2                42
    ```

    f. This divisibility test is more useful with three digit numbers. For example:

    $581 \Rightarrow 58 - 2 \times 1 = 56$ and since 56 is divisible by 7, then 581 is divisible by 7.

    Likewise:

    $635 \Rightarrow 63 - 2 \times 5 = 53$ and since 53 is not divisible by 7, then 635 is not divisible by 7.

3. There is a divisibility test for 11. For example, **6**5**6**3**7** is divisible by 11. To use the test, sum every other digit, then take the difference in the two sums: The sum of the digits in bold print is 6 + 6 + 7 = 19. The sum of the underlined digits is 5 + 3 = 8. Now take the positive difference in the two sums and see if the result is divisible by 11. Since 19 - 8 = 11 and 11 is divisible by 11, then 65,637 is divisible by 11.

    ✎ Answer questions 12 through 14 on the Student Worksheet.

Name _____

Date _____

Activity 3

A Prime Investigation with 7, 11, and 13

Part 1 - The Investigation

1. In step 1, was your number divisible by 7? _____

2. Was your number divisible by 11? _____

3. Was your number divisible by 13? _____

    What did you notice about the new quotient?

    _____

4. Would the order that you divided by 7, 11, or 13 affect your result? Try dividing your original number by these divisors in different orders. Write a sentence on your findings.

    _____

    _____

5. Did everyone in your group pick a number that was divisible by 7, 11, and 13?

    _____

    If so, discuss within your group why you think everyone's number was divisible by 7, 11, 13. Write a sentence or two explaining why you think these special six digit numbers are divisible by 7, 11, and 13.

    _____

    _____

    _____

Part 2 - Justifying why numbers are divisible by 7, 11, and 13

6. Write a sentence explaining your findings from Part 2 #1 (page 26).

    _____

    _____

    _____

7. Describe the relationship between the product in step 4 (page 26) and these special six-digit numbers.

_____

_____

_____

8. Rewrite your three-digit numbers as the product of the number and 1001. Then write it out using the distributive property, as shown on page 26.

_____

_____

9. Explain why you know 468,468 is divisible by 7, 11, and 13.

_____

_____

10. Explain how to mentally multiply 369 by 1001.

_____

_____

Part 3 - Divisibility Tests

11. Write the divisibility tests for 2, 3, and 5.

_____

_____

_____

12. Show how to use the divisibility test for 11 to see if your original six-digit number is divisible by 11.

_____

13. Is 852,345 divisible by 11? _____

Show how to use this divisibility test to examine 852,345 for divisibility by 11.

_____

_____

14. Number theorists have developed divisibility rules or tests for many different numbers. Can you write a divisibility test for a six-digit number to be divisible by 1001?

_____

_____

Teacher Notes

Activity 3

A Prime Investigation with 7, 11, and 13

Math Strand

♦ Number sense

Materials

♦ TI-73 calculator
♦ Student Worksheets (page 28)

Students will investigate uncommon divisibility tests. They will also discover an interesting characteristic of six-digit multiples of 1001. The distributive property will be applied to unravel the mystery.

Vocabulary

divisible	A number is divisible by another if, when dividing the remainder is zero.
factors	The numbers multiplied in a multiplication problem.
distributive property	For any real numbers a, b, and c, a(b+ c) = ab + ac.

Classroom Management

Students should understand the concept of divisibility and know the divisibility rules for 2, 3, and 5. This activity can be student- or teacher-directed. If student-directed, group students in teams of 3 or 4. Students should be instructed to work independently but could confer with their team when prompted by the activity. You should monitor and observe the student groups to make sure they understand the task. Make sure students initially understand what kind of number to start with. A wrap-up may include questioning students on why these six-digit numbers are multiples of 7, 11, and 13.

Activity

Part 1 - The Investigation (sample answers with some teacher tips)

1. Make sure the students understand the function and display of integer divide [INT÷]. If they have not been exposed to this function, explain using a simpler problem. Yes, their number should be divisible by 7.

2. Make sure the students understand the display of the screen shot in number 2. If they are not familiar with using previous answers, show some simpler examples. Yes, their number should be divisible by 11.

3. Yes, their number should be divisible by 13. The new quotient is the original three-digit number.

Part 2 - Justify why these number are divisible by 7, 11, and 13
(sample answers with some teacher tips)

1. Their six-digit number abc,abc should be divisible by 7, 11, and 13.

2. 7 x 11 x 13 = 1001

3. abc,abc ÷ 1001 = abc

4. abc x 1001 = abc,abc
   The original six-digit number - abc,abc. It is the same.

Part 3 - Divisibility Tests (sample answers with some teacher tips)

1. A number is divisible by 2 if it is even or if the ones digit is 0, 2, 4, 6, or 8.
   A number is divisible by 3 if the sum of the digits are divisible by 3.
   A number is divisible by 5 if the ones digit is a 0 or a 5.

2. This procedure is presented as a bit of trivia. It is especially useless with a calculator in hand.

Answers to Student Worksheet

1. Yes, their number should be divisible by 7.

2. Yes, their number should be divisible by 11.

3. Yes, their number should be divisible by 13. The new quotient is the original three-digit number.

4. No, the order you divide by 7, 11, 13 would not affect the result. It doesn't matter what order you divide in because you are dividing by the same composite number of 1001.

5. Yes, they should have. If they did not, inspect their number. If you multiply 7 x 11 x 13 you get 1001 and if you take 1001 times any three-digit number you get a six-digit number where the original three-digit number repeats. Therefore, your original six-digit number would be divisible by 1001 or 7, 11, and 13.

6. Their six-digit number abc,abc should be divisible by 7, 11, and 13.

7. The original six-digit number - abc,abc. It is the same.

8. abc x 1001 = abc x (1000 + 1)

   = abc x 1000 + abc x 1

   = abc, 000 + abc

   = abc,abc

9. Since 468,468 = 468 x 1001 and 1001= 7 x 11 x 13 then 468,468 is divisible by 7, 11, and 13.

10. $369 \times 1001 = 369 \times (1000 + 1)$

$\quad = 369 \times 1000 + 369 \times 1$

$\quad = 369{,}000 + 369$

$\quad = 369{,}369$

11. A number is divisible by 2 if it is even or if the ones digit is 0, 2, 4, 6, or 8.
A number is divisible by 3 if the sum of the digits are divisible by 3.
A number is divisible by 5 if the ones digit is a 0 or a 5.

12. In A B̲ C, A̲ B C̲, take the sum of every other digit and then subtract. If the difference is divisible by 11 then the original number is.
(A + B + C) - (A̲+ B̲+ C̲) = 0 and 0 is divisible by 11 so the original number is divisible by 11.

13. No. Since $8 + 2 + 4 = 14$ and $5 + 3 + 5 = 13$ and $14 - 13 = 1$ and 1 is NOT divisible by 11, then 852,345 is not divisible by 11.

14. A six-digit number is divisible by 1001 if it is in the form abc,abc.

Activity 4

Oliver's Method

Objective

♦ To discover a relationship between the Greatest Common Factor (GCF) and the Least Common Multiple (LCM) of two numbers

Materials

♦ TI-73 calculator

♦ Student Worksheet

In this activity you will:

♦ find a relationship between Greatest Common Factor (GCF) and Least Common Multiple (LCM)

♦ justify why Oliver's method works

You will need to know this math vocabulary:

♦ greatest common factor (GCF) also known as greatest common divisor (GCD)

♦ least common multiple (LCM)

♦ prime factorization

♦ relatively prime

♦ multiplicative inverse or reciprocal

Introduction

Is there a relationship between Greatest Common Factors (GCF) and Least Common Multiples (LCM)? Oliver Richard came up with his own unique method of finding the LCM after the GCF is known.

This is what he does. To find the LCM of 20 and 36:

Step 1: Write the two numbers as a fraction $\dfrac{20}{36}$

Step 2: Simplify the fraction $\dfrac{20 \div 4}{36 \div 4} = \dfrac{5}{9}$

Step 3: Take the original fraction and multiply it by the reciprocal of the simplified fraction $\dfrac{20 \times 9}{36 \times 5} = \dfrac{180}{180}$

180 is the LCM of 20 and 36.

Problem

Through repeated examples on Table 1 of the Student Worksheet, you will look for a relationship between the GCF, LCM, and the two numbers. You will then discuss your findings with your group. Your second task will be to justify why Oliver's method works or doesn't work.

Activity

1. Go to the Home screen ([2nd] [QUIT]) and press [CLEAR]. You will find the LCM of 20 and 36 on the calculator. Press [MATH] [ENTER] and type **2 0** [,] **3 6** [)] [ENTER].

2. To find the GCD of two numbers, follow the same steps as screen shots at the right except select **2:gcd(**. Press [MATH], select **2:gcd(** and type **2 0** [,] **3 6** [)] [ENTER].

    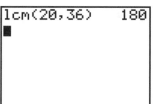

    ✎ Go to the Student Worksheet and complete Table 1 using the calculator's LCM and GCD functions. Answer questions 1 through 4 on the Student Worksheet.

3. Test Oliver's method using some of the problems in Table 1. Set [MODE] as shown at the right. Enter **16** [b/c] **40** [ENTER]. Press [SIMP] [ENTER] [SIMP] [ENTER] [SIMP] [ENTER] until the numerator and denominator are **relatively prime**. (GCF of the numerator and denominator is 1.)

4. Type in the original fraction and multiply it by its simplified reciprocal. This shows that the product of a number and it's **reciprocal** (or **multiplicative inverse**) is 1. Next find the unsimplifed form of 1 by breaking the multiplication into numerator times numerator and denominator times denominator.

    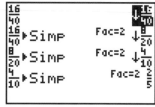

    ✎ Answer questions 5 through 8 on the Student Worksheet.

    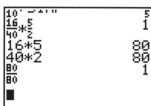

Name _____

Date _____

Activity 4

Oliver's Method

Record your results on the table below. Then answer the questions about the activity.

Table 1

(a, b)	GCD	LCM	GCD x LCM	a x b
(16,40)				
(18,72)				
(9,12)				
(7,5)				
(6,20)				
(8,16)				
(15, 9)				
(11, 12)				
(36, 48)				
(16,14)				

1. How is the product of the two numbers (**a** and **b**) related to the product of the GCD and the LCM of the two numbers?

   _____

2. Justify your conclusion.
   Hint: You may want to examine the **prime factorization**.

   a   x   b   GCD   x   LCD

   _____

   _____

3. Suppose you have a four-function calculator that will only add, subtract, multiply and divide. You know that the GCD of 40 and 48 is 8 and you need to know the LCM. Explain the keystrokes you could use on the calculator to find it.

   _____

   _____

   _____

4. James and Andy are training for a bike race. James can go around the park on the bike path in 20 minutes and Andy can go the same distance in 16 minutes. If they start at the same time, when will they be side-by-side again? Write a mathematical expression you could use to answer this question.

   _____

   _____

   _____

5. Use Oliver's method to find the LCM of 18 and 72.

   Step 1: Write as fraction _____

   Step 2: Simplify_____
   How do you simplify fractions?

   _____

   Step 3: Multiply the original fraction by the reciprocal of the simplified fraction to get the LCM

   _____

6. Use Oliver's method to find the LCM of 9 and 12. Show the process.

   _____

   _____

7. Write an equation that describes the relationship between a, b, GCD, and LCM that you saw in Table 1.

   _____

8. How can you change the equation to make it fit Oliver's method?

   _____

   _____

Teacher Notes

Activity 4

Oliver's Method

Math Strand

♦ Number sense

♦ Algebraic reasoning

Materials

♦ TI-73 calculators

♦ Student Worksheets (page 35)

Students will find and justify the relationship that the product of two numbers is equal to the product of the LCM and the GCF.

Vocabulary

Greatest Common Factor(GCF) or Greatest Common Divisor(GCD)	The greatest factor or divisor common to a set of two or more numbers
Least Common Multiple (LCM)	The least of the nonzero common multiples of two or more numbers
prime number	A number greater than 1 that has exactly two factors, 1 and itself.
prime factorization	The process of writing a composite number as the product of prime factors.
relatively prime	Two or more numbers whose GCF is 1.
multiplicative inverse or reciprocal	The product of a number and its multiplicative inverse is 1.

Classroom Management

Students may work independently on Table 1 and discuss their findings in groups of 3 to 4. Working in their groups, they will answer the questions on the Student Worksheet. Students should have prior experience in finding GCF and LCM by the traditional methods of listing and prime factorization. This activity is an example of a student who developed a unique way of performing this common middle school skill. The justification of this algorithm may provide a missing link of the connection between the GCF, LCM, and the product of the two numbers.

Activity

The directions and keystrokes on the student activity pages are complete.

Answers to Student Worksheet

1. They are equal.

2. Prime Factorization.

a	x	b		GCD	x	LCM
16	x	20		4	x	80

$$4 \text{ x } 4 \text{ x } 4 \text{ x } 5 \qquad\qquad 2 \text{ x } 2 \text{ x } 4 \text{ x } 20$$

$$2 \text{ x } 2 \text{ x } 2 \text{ x } 2 \text{ x } 2 \text{ x } 2 \text{ x } 5 \qquad 2 \text{ x } 2 \text{ x } 2 \text{ x } 2 \text{ x } 5 \text{ x } 2 \text{ x } 2$$

$$320 = 2 \text{ x } 2 \text{ x } 2 \text{ x } 2 \text{ x } 2 \text{ x } 2 \text{ x } 5 \qquad 320 = 2 \text{ x } 2 \text{ x } 2 \text{ x } 2 \text{ x } 5 \text{ x } 2 \text{ x } 2$$

3. $40 \text{ x } 48 \div 8$

4. 80 minutes or 1 hour 20 minutes; The mathematical expression is $16 \text{ x } 20 \div 4 = 80$ minutes or 1 hour 20 minutes.

5. Use Oliver's method to find the LCM of 18 and 72.

   a. Step 1: Write as a fraction $\dfrac{18}{72}$.

   b. Step 2: Simplify: $\dfrac{1}{4}$ How do you simplify fractions? Divide by GCF.

   c. Step 3: Multiply original fraction by reciprocal of simplified fraction to get the LCM.

   $$\frac{18 \times 4 = 72}{72 \times 1 = 72}$$

6. $\dfrac{9}{12} : \dfrac{3}{4} : \dfrac{9 \times 4 = 36}{12 \times 3 = 36}$

7. a x b = GCF x LCM

8. a ÷ GCF x b = LCM or b ÷ GCF x a = LCM

Objective

♦ To understand Euclid's method of finding the Greatest Common Factor

Activity 5

Materials

♦ TI-73 calculator

♦ Student Worksheet

It's Greek to Me

In this activity you will:

♦ use Euclid's way to find the GCF (GCD) of large numbers

♦ investigate how this method works with the integer divide function on the TI-73

You will need to know this math vocabulary:

♦ greatest common divisor (GCD) or greatest common factor (GCF)

♦ prime number

♦ composite

♦ prime factorization

Problem

This is how you can use Euclid's method to find the GCD of 105 and 975.

Step 1: Divide the larger number by the smaller number

Step 2: Successively divide the divisor by the previous remainder

Step 3: Continue the process until you arrive at a remainder of 0. The last divisor will be the GCD.

$$
\begin{array}{r}
9 \\
105\overline{)975} \\
-945 \\
\hline
30
\end{array}
\quad
\begin{array}{r}
3 \\
30\overline{)105} \\
-90 \\
\hline
15
\end{array}
\quad
\begin{array}{r}
2 \\
15\overline{)30} \\
-30 \\
\hline
0
\end{array}
$$

Activity

1. You will use the integer divide function on the calculator to find the GCD of two numbers. Set [MODE] to **Float** before you begin. Then press [2nd] [QUIT][CLEAR]. Type **9 7 5** [2nd][INT÷] **1 0 5** [ENTER]. Repeat the keystrokes to divide the previous divisor (105) by the previous remainder (15) as shown below until you arrive at a remainder of 0. The last divisor used will be the GCD.

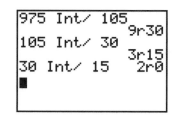

2. Recall other ways you have learned to find the GCF (GCD). Prime factorization is probably the most emphasized method. You may have learned to make a tree diagram to prime factorize a composite number. However, using divisibility rules, the calculator, and writing down the prime factors as you divide can save you some space on your paper. It is important to keep your prime factors in order and to keep yourself organized. Start dividing by the smallest prime factors first and go in increasing order until you get a quotient of 1.

3. To find GCF using prime factorization, write 105 and 975 as the product of prime factors. Find the factors (divisors) that are common to both and multiply them.

   105 = 3 x 5 x 7

   975 = 3 x 5 x 5 x 13

   GCF = 3 x 5 = 15

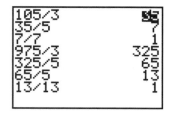

4. The first way you probably learned how to find GCF was by making lists and finding the greatest divisor common to both. You can use the prime factorization above and combinations of the factors to list the factors of 105 and 975.

   105 { 1, 3, 5 ,7, 3 x 5, 3 x 7, 5 x 7, 3 x 5 x 7 } or { 1, 3, 5, 7, **15**, 21, 35, 105}

   975 { 1, 3, 5, 13, 3x5, 5x5, 3x13, 5x13, 3x5x5, 3x5x13, 5x5x13, 3x5x5x13}
   or

   {1, 3, 5, 13, **15**, 25, 39, 65, 75, 195, 325, 975}

   Inspecting the lists verifies that 15 is the greatest divisor (factor).

5. Another way to check your result is to use the GCD function on the calculator.
   Press [MATH] **2:gcd(** 105,975 [)] [ENTER].

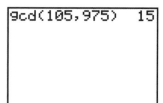

✎ Go to the Student Worksheet and answer the questions.

Name _____

Date _____

Activity 5

It's Greek to Me

Answer the questions about this activity.

Use Euclid's algorithm and integer divide to solve the following problems. Show your steps.

1. GCD (220, 2924)

_____

_____

_____

2. GCD (14,595, 10,856)

_____

_____

_____

3. Find the GCD of 1120 and 2860 two different ways: Euclid's way and Prime Factorization.

Euclid's Method	Prime Factorization
2860 [INT÷] 1120 =	2860 = 1120 = GCF =
1120 [INT÷] 620 =	1120 = 620 = GCF =
620 [INT÷] 500 =	620 = 500 = GCF =
500 [INT÷] 120 =	500 = 120 = GCF =
120 [INT÷] 20 =	120 = 20= GCF =

4. Compare the methods in problem 3 above. What patterns do you see?

_____

_____

5. Show four different ways to find GCD (105, 42).

_____

_____

_____

_____

Teacher Notes

Activity 5

It's Greek to Me

Math Strand

♦ Number sense

♦ Numeration

Materials

♦ TI-73 calculator

♦ Student Worksheets (page 41)

Students will review finding GCF using prime factorization and listing. They will investigate Euclid's algorithm of finding GCF and compare to methods already learned.

Vocabulary

Greatest Common Divisor (GCD) or Greatest Common Factor (GCF)	The greatest of the common factors or divisors of two or more numbers.
prime number	A number greater than 1 that has exactly two factors, 1 and itself.
composite	Any whole number that has more than two factors.
prime factorization	The process of writing a composite number as the product of prime factors.

Classroom Management

Students should have experienced finding GCF using the listing and prime factorization methods before doing this activity. This method works the best when trying to find the GCD of large numbers that are fairly close together.

Greatest Common Factor and Greatest Common Divisor are used interchangeably to reinforce the idea that they are synonyms.

Activity

The directions and keystrokes on the student activity pages are complete.

Answers to Student Worksheet

1. 2924 INT/ 220 = 13 R 64 ;   220 INT/ 64 = 3 R 28;   64 INT/ 28 = 2 R 8;

28 INT/ 8 = 3 R 4;   8 INT/ 4 = 2 R 0   So GCD = 4

2. GCD (14,595, 10,856) = GCD (10,856, 3739) = GCD (3739, 3378) = GCD (3378, 361) = GCD (361, 129) = GCD (129, 103) = GCD (103, 26) = GCD (26, 25) =

GCD (25,1)=1

3. See table below.

Euclid's Method	Prime Factorization
2860 [INT÷] 1120 = 2 r 620	2860 = 2 x 2 x 5 x 11 x 13 1120 = 2 x 2 x 2 x 2 x 2 x 5 x 7 **GCF** = 2 x 2 x 5 = 20
1120 [INT÷] 620 = 1 r 500	1120 = 2 x 2 x 2 x 2 x 2 x 5 x 7 620 = 2 x 2 x 5 x 31 **GCF** = 2 x 2 x 5 = 20
620 [INT÷] 500 = 1 r 120	620 = 2 x 2 x 5 x 31 500 =2 x 2 x 5 x 5 x 5 **GCF** = 2 x 2 x 5 = 20
500 [INT÷] 120 = 4 r 20	500 = 2 x 2 x 5 x 5 x 5 120 = 2 x 2 x 2 x 3 x 5 **GCF** = 2 x 2 x 5 = 20
120 [INT÷] 20 = 6 r 0	120 = 2 x 2 x 5 20= 2 x 2 x 2 x 3 x 5 **GCF** = 2 x 2 x 5 = 20

4. Answers will vary. In each step of Euclid's method you will get the same GCF. So you are just simplifying the problem by successively dividing. The GCF remains a factor until the end.

5. Answers will vary.

   a. The easiest and quickest way is to use the TI-73 calculator. Press MATH, then select **2:gcd(** and type in the numbers separated by a comma. (**2:gcd(105 ⌐ 42**) The result is 21.

   b. A second way is to use Euclid's way and integer divide on the calculator: **105** [INT÷] **42 = 2 r 21; 42** [INT÷] **21 = 2 r 0.** The last divisor when the remainder is 0 is the GCD. Therefore, 21 is the GCD.

c. Another method is to prime factorize, then find the divisors common to both numbers and multiply them

105 = 3 x 5 x 7

42 = 2 x 3 x 7

GCF = 3 x 7 = 21

d. A fourth method is to list the factors of both numbers and find the greatest common to both lists.

105 { 1, 3, 5, 7, 15, **21**, 35, 105}

42   { 1, 2, 3, 6, 7, 14, **21**, 42}

Going Further

1. Examine these relationships:

GCD(16,20) and GCD(16, 36)

GCD(24,36) and GCD(24, 60)

GCD(18,10) and GCD(18,28)

a. What do you notice?

b. What is the relationship between the two sets of numbers in each example? (If you add the two numbers in the 1st pair, you get the last number of the second pair. Since the first integer division of each pair has the same remainder, the GCD is also the same.)

2. Find out more information about Euclid and his mathematical contributions and report to the class.

3. Find the GCD (120,75,105) using the Euclidean Algorithm applied to two numbers at a time.

4. Have the students write the process of Euclid's algorithm in words as if they were explaining it to a student who was absent.

EXPLORATIONS

Activity 6

Class of Gold

Objective

♦ To investigate Fibonacci numbers and the ratios of successive Fibonacci numbers

Materials

♦ TI-73 calculator

♦ Meter stick

♦ Student Worksheet

In this activity you will:

♦ take measurements of two different heights

♦ investigate the relationship of these two heights (a person's height and the height of that person's navel)

♦ examine a graph (scatterplot) of these two measurements

You will need to be familiar with this math vocabulary:

♦ ratio

♦ proportion

♦ Fibonacci numbers

♦ the Golden Ratio

Introduction

Patterns occur in nature and in all branches of science. **Fibonacci numbers** (1, 1, 2, 3, 5, 8, 13…) appear in many places in mathematics, and ratios of successive Fibonacci numbers are found in various measurements. Some people have long bodies and short legs while others may have short bodies and long legs. There are advantages and disadvantages to both types of proportion. Can you name some?

Problem

Here are the first seven terms of the Fibonacci sequence:

1, 1, 2, 3, 5, 8, 13.

On a separate piece of paper, write the next 13 terms.

Activity

1. Enter terms (1-20) in **L1**. Then, enter terms 2-21 in **L2**. Use the shortcut of pasting **L1** in **L2**, deleting the first term in **L2** and adding a 21st term at the bottom of list. To do this, highlight **L2**, press $\boxed{\text{2nd}}$ [STAT] and select **1: L1** $\boxed{\text{ENTER}}$. Don't forget to add the 21st term in as the 20th element in **L2**.

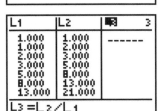

2. Find the ratio of successive Fibonacci numbers as decimals rounded to the nearest thousandth.

   a. Set the $\boxed{\text{MODE}}$ to 3 decimal places.

   b. Let **L3** = **L2**/ **L1** by highlighting **L3** and entering the formula **L2**/ **L1**, and then pressing $\boxed{\text{ENTER}}$. (See the screen at the right.)

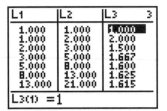

   c. Scroll down **L3**. What do you notice about these ratios as you go down the list?

   Do you notice that the numbers approach 1.618? This is the approximated value of the **Golden Ratio**. The Golden Ratio is prevalent in Greek architecture and is found in rectangles and in other geometric shapes.

3. According to some statisticians, the ratio of a person's height to the height of their navel should be close to the Golden Ratio (1.618) if the person is properly proportioned.

   a. You and your partner will now measure each other and find these two heights to the nearest tenth of a centimeter. Then find the ratio of the two numbers. For example, if your height is 7mm marks past 161 cm, then call it 161.7 cm.

   ✎ Go to the Student Worksheet and record the measurements.

   b. Give your name and your heights to the teacher to be recorded on the teacher's transparency.

   ✎ When your teacher displays the class data, copy it on Table 1 of your Student Worksheet.

4. Name a list **HT**. To do this, press ⌷LIST⌷ and scroll over to the first empty list. Press ⌷2nd⌷⌷TEXT⌷, use the cursor to select **H**, press ⌷ENTER⌷, select **T**, press ⌷ENTER⌷, select **Done** ⌷ENTER⌷ ⌷ENTER⌷. Name a list to the right of this list as **NHT** for navel height using similar keystrokes. The third list name that corresponds to Table 1 will be called **HTNHT** to stand for **HT ÷ NHT**.

   a. Enter class students' heights in list **HT** and navel heights in a list **NHT**. Then find the ratio of **HT÷ NHT**. To do this press ⌷2nd⌷⌷STAT⌷, select **HT** ⌷ENTER⌷⌷÷⌷⌷2nd⌷⌷STAT⌷ **NHT**, select ⌷ENTER⌷. Record these ratios in the fourth column of Table 1.

   ✎ Answer questions 1 and 2 on the Student Worksheet.

   b. Find the mean average of your classes ratios. Press ⌷2nd⌷⌷STAT⌷ ⌷▶⌷ ⌷▶⌷ to **Math**, select **3:mean(**, then type **LHTNHT** and press ⌷ENTER⌷.

   ✎ Answer question 3 on the Student Worksheet.

5. You can determine relationships between two quantities like height and navel height using the TI-73. Create a Scatterplot of navel height vs. Height. The person's navel height will be on the horizontal axes and their height will be on the vertical axes. Before setting up the graph, press ⌷2nd⌷ ⌷PLOT⌷ and select **4: Plotsoff** ⌷ENTER⌷ to turn the plots off. You will work on Plot 1. Press ⌷2nd⌗ ⌷PLOT⌷ and select **1: Plot1...On** to turn Plot 1 on. Define Plot 1 as shown at the right.

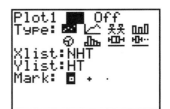

   a. Set an appropriate window remembering that the **X** values are the navel heights and the **Y** values are the student heights. Note that **Xmin** and **Xmax** refer to the minimum and maximum values on the horizontal axis and **Ymin** and **Ymax** refer to the vertical axis. **Xscl** and **Yscl** defines the distance between tick marks on the axis.

   b. Before viewing the graph, press ⌷Y=⌷ and make sure that all the equations are turned off. Now press ⌷GRAPH⌷. ⌷TRACE⌷ the graph and find the data point that represents your navel height and height.

   ✎ Using your window parameters, sketch the graph in the window provided in question 4 on the Student Worksheet. Label the axis with a few reference numbers.

6. Now you will place a line on the plotted data. This line would represent a graph if everyone was proportionally the same. You will use the **Manual-Fit** option of the TI-73.

   a. From the Home screen, press ⌷2nd⌷⌷STAT⌷ ⌷◀⌷ ⌷2nd⌷ ⌷VARS⌷ **2:Y-Vars** then **1:Y1** ⌷ENTER⌷ ⌷ENTER⌷. Position the cursor at the beginning of the line you want to draw, then press ⌷ENTER⌷.

b. As you press the cursor keys, the line is drawn and the slope or steepness is adjusted. When you have matched the plotted points as desired, press ENTER. You can use the cursor keys to adjust the line if you are not happy with where you placed it.

c. When you find the best fit, press ENTER again.

The equation of this line has now been pasted in the Y= editor in **Y1**. This is an approximated equation that describes the relationship between the classes' navel heights and student heights.

✎ Answer questions 5, 6, and 7 on the Student Worksheet.

d. If Y= Height, X= Navel Height and Y ÷X = 1.618 then Y= _____. This would be an equation of a line that would describe all people that are proportioned according to the golden ratio. Type this equation into **Y2**. Press GRAPH.

✎ Answer questions 8 and 9 on the Student Worksheet.

7. Use the mean average of the class to write an equation in **Y3**. Type in the number you found to be the mean in **Y3** and then press x to follow it. Press GRAPH.

✎ Answer questions 10, 11, and 12 on the Student Worksheet.

8. What if the measurements were all taken in inches, would the ratio change? To investigate this, convert the measurements in **LHT** and **LNHT** to inches.

a. Go to **LIST**. Name 2 new lists **HIN** (height in inches) and **NIN** (navel height in inches). Go to the top of the list **HIN**, highlighting **HIN**, press ENTER to select the list you want to convert (**LHT**) in 2nd[STAT]. Press 2nd [CONVERT] select **1:Length** ENTER, select **2:cm**, then **4:inch** and ENTER again. Do the same thing with the list called **NHT**.

b. Next, take the ratio of **HIN** to **NIN** into a list named **RATIO**. Compare this **RATIO** list to the ratios in the list named **HTNHT**. Explain your findings in question 13.
Note: To make the lists easier to compare paste **HTNHT** to the right of **RATIO**.

✎ Answer questions 14, 15, and 16 on the Student Worksheet.

Activity 6

Class of Gold

Record your results on the table below. Then answer the questions about the activity.

My height in centimeters is _____

The height of my navel is _____

My height (Ht)/ Navel height (NHt) = _____

Table 1

Name	Height (cm) ʟHT	Navel Height (cm) ʟNHT	Height/ Navel Ht. ʟHTNHT

1. Which ratio is the "most golden"? Justify your answer with a reason.

    _____

    _____

2. Which ratio is the "least golden"? Justify your answer with a reason.

    _____

    _____

3. Find the mean average of the **HTNHT** list. How golden is your class?

    _____

    _____

4. Sketch the graph of navel height verse student height. Make sure to label the axes and use numbers to show the values on number lines.

5. In general, as navel height increases, what happens to student height?

    _____

    _____

6. Write the equation of the line that has been pasted in the Y= editor.

    _____

    _____

7. The number in front of the x in the equation is defined as the ratio of change in y over change in x. How does this number compare to the Golden ratio?

    _____

    _____

8. If Y= Height, X= Navel Height and $Y \div X = 1.618$ then Y= _____

9. Are there any similarities between **Y1** and **Y2**? Explain.

    _____

    _____

10. Are there any similarities between **Y1, Y2,** and **Y3**? Explain.

_____

_____

_____

11. Based on the relationship of a person that fits a truly golden proportion, which equation would you use to find their height?

_____

12. Find the height of a truly "golden" person whose navel height is 100 cm.

_____

13. How does the ratio of height to navel height in centimeters compare to the ratio of height to navel height in inches?

_____

_____

14. Write a paragraph on how you could predict your height in three years if your navel height increases by 10 centimeters.

_____

_____

15. Sketch a graph of the lines of **Y1, Y2,** and **Y3.**

16. If the golden ratio (1.618) represents a person whose height is perfectly proportionally to their leg length discuss the possible ratios of people with long legs and short bodies and short legs and long bodies.

_____

_____

_____

_____

_____

Teacher Notes

Activity 6

Class of Gold

Math Strand

- ◆ Patterns and functions
- ◆ Algebraic reasoning

Materials

- ◆ TI-73 calculator
- ◆ Meter sticks
- ◆ Rulers
- ◆ Student Worksheet (page 51)
- ◆ Teacher transparency (page 51)

Students will investigate Fibonacci numbers and the ratios of successive Fibonacci numbers. They will take measurements of their height and their navel heights and investigate the relationship between the two. Finally, they will examine a scatterplot and a linear relationship fitted to the data points.

Vocabulary

ratio	The comparison of two numbers by division.
proportion	An equation that involves equal ratios.
Fibonacci numbers	A pattern of numbers generated by adding two successive numbers to obtain the next. {1, 1, 2, 3, 5, 8, 13, 21, 34, 55, 89, 144, 233, 377, 610, 987, 1597...}
The Golden Ratio	$\dfrac{\sqrt{5}+1}{2}$ which is approximately equal to 1.618.

Classroom Management

After measurements are taken, this activity could be totally teacher-directed, or the students could do the investigation in pairs or small groups. However, you may want to introduce the activity with the opening paragraph. Middle school students can be sensitive to their body proportions. You may want to have the students discuss how important it is that everyone is unique as well as the advantages and disadvantages of both proportions described in the opening paragraph. When pairing students to take measurements, you may want to pair girls with girls and boys with boys. When measuring the height of their navels have the students hold a ruler perpendicular to the navel so the other student does not have to find it.

Activity

1. For instructions on accessing a list, see Appendix A. You may want to make sure that the students have turned off stat plots, cleared any equations out of the equation editor, and executed the SetUp Editor before they begin this activity. Press 2nd [PLOT] **4: PlotsOff** ENTER Y= and scroll down and press CLEAR to remove equations. To execute the Setup Editor, press 2nd [CATALOG] and scroll down to **SetUpEditor**, then press ENTER.

2. For more information on using formulas in lists, see Appendix C. If students use the formula **L3 = L2/L1** and get a **dim mismatch** error, then they probably forgot to enter the 21st Fibonacci number as the 20th element in **L2**, or **L1** and **L2** do not contain the same number of elements.

3. Have a transparency of Table 1 available for students to record their heights.

4. For more information on naming lists, see Appendix B. The screen at the right shows sample data of heights and navel heights.

    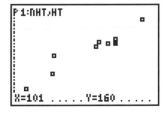

    To find the ratio of **HT** to **NHT**, you may want to have the students put the formula in quotes. This will allow students to view the formula at the top of the list and will automatically change the ratio if you find someone measured inaccurately and you go in and change a measurement in one of the lists in the formula.

5. Students may need help setting an appropriate window depending on their experience. You may want them to use ZOOM **7:ZoomStat**, but it is very important that students learn how to determine range and scaling when drawing graphs. (If they need help, have them begin by entering the smallest value from **NHT** for **Xmin** and the largest value from **NHT** for **Xmax**. Do the same for **Ymin** and **Ymax,** using the values from **HT**.)

    Sample data of a scatterplot is at the right.

6. Sample data of **Y1**, **Y2**, and **Y3**. The last screen shot appears to be one line but it is all three.

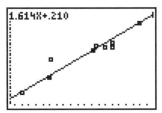

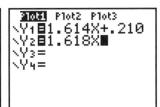

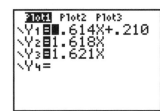 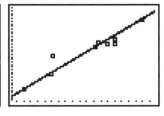

7. If **Conversion** function has never been used, you may want to have the students convert their measurements in centimeters to inches (or vice-versa). They will do this on the Home screen.

  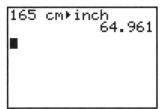

Answers to Student Worksheet

1. Answers will vary. It should be the ratio closest to 1.618.

2. Answers will vary. It should be the ratio the furthest from 1.618.

3. Answers will vary. It should be close to 1.6.

4. See student sketch.

5. It increases.

6. Answers will vary.

7. It should be fairly close to 1.618.

8. Y=1.618 X

9. Answers will vary. They should look close to the same line.

10. Answers will vary. They should all look close to the same line.

11. Y=1.618 X

12. 100 cm x 1.618 = 161.8 cm

13. It is the same.

14. Add 10 cm to present navel height and multiply it by the person's ratio.

15. See sketch.

16. A ratio greater than 1.618 would indicate the person has shorter legs and a longer body. A ratio less than 1.618 would indicate the person has longer legs and a shorter body.

Going Further

Have students investigate where Fibonacci numbers and the golden ratio are found in nature and in science.

Depending on the level of student, you may want to have them solve this quadratic equation to derive the algebraic representation of the golden ratio. The ratio *of 1 to a positive number is equal to the ratio of the number to 1 minus the number.*

$$\frac{1}{x} = \frac{x}{1-x}$$

$$1 - x = x^2$$

$$x^2 + x - 1 = 0$$

Using the quadratic formula you find x = $\dfrac{\sqrt{5}+1}{2}$

Activity 7

Go for the Gold

Objective

♦ To explore and use ratios

Materials

♦ TI-73 calculator

♦ Ruler that measures to the nearest millimeter

♦ String

♦ Student Worksheet

In this activity you will:

♦ find ratios that are known to be "golden"

♦ take measurements of facial features

You will need to know this math vocabulary:

♦ ratio

♦ mean

Introduction

The human body is filled with "hidden" ratios that seem to remain constant for most people. Some examples are the arm span/height and the circumference of the fist/foot length.

You know what a ratio is and how to find it. The Greeks knew this, too, and they were in love with a particular ratio called *The Golden Ratio*, whose value is 1.618 to three decimal places.

Activity

You will be rounding your results to three decimal places. Before you begin, set the MODE to 3 places.

Part 1 - Individual Activity

1. The Greeks liked to make their statues with Golden Ratios twinkling in them. To see how they did this, measure the distances between features on the statue picture as accurately as you can *to the nearest millimeter*, writing the answer as a decimal number of centimeters.

✎ Record each measurement on the Student Worksheet.

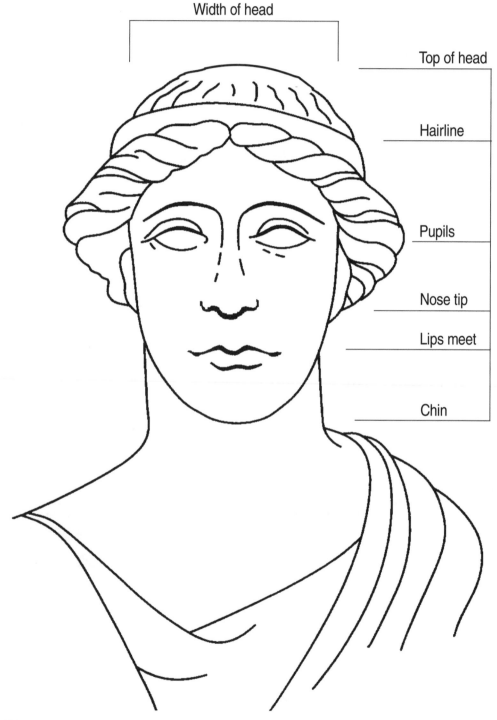

Use your ruler to find each measurement to the nearest millimeter (___.___ cm). If something is 7mm marks past 3 cm, call it 3.7 cm.

Part 2 - Group Project

Have a team member measure lengths on your face while recording the information in #3 on the Student Worksheet.

> ***Note to Measurer***: It is best to hold the ruler as far away from your eyes as possible when measuring these distances on the other's face. Otherwise you will get distorted measurements. Another way to measure is to use string.

Part 3

✎ Record your mean average ratios, your group's mean average ratios, and your class' mean average ratio in the table on the Student Worksheet.

Going Further

1. Draw a strange face, but make sure it has lots of Golden Ratios in it.

2. Redraw the Greek face so that it has none of the Golden Ratios in it.

3. Make up a new ratio and give it an interesting name. You can even make up some history and lore about it in a write-up. Draw a face that has lots of this ratio. Compare and contrast it with the Golden Ratio Face.

4. Find photographs in magazines and books. Check them for the Golden Ratios you measured in the Greek face. Find faces of other nationalities and see if they have more or fewer Golden Ratios than the ideal Greek one.

5. Purchase or borrow from the library a copy of *Jim and the Beanstalk* by Ray Briggs. In this story, Jim wakes up one day to find a great plant growing outside his window. He decides to climb up into the clouds, where he finds a castle with an old, unhappy giant. Unlike the original *Jack in the Beanstalk* tale, in this story, Jim helps the aging giant. When the giant complains about not being able to see to read, Jim measures his huge head and returns to his town to have giant eyeglasses made. Later, he measures the giant for false teeth and a wig. The proportional illustrations help students as they work to figure out the size of the giant's hands and then his height.

Name _____

Date _____

Activity 7

Go for the Gold

1. Record your measurements from the illustration on page 60.

    A. Top of Head to Chin =____.____cm

    B. Top of Head to Pupil = _____.____cm

    C. Pupil to Tip of Nose = ____ . ___ cm

    D. Pupil to Lips = ____.___ cm

    E. Width of Nose = ____.____cm

    F. Distance Between Outside Edges of Eyes = ____.____cm

    G. Width of Head = _____.____cm

    H. Hairline to Pupil = _____._____cm

    I. Tip of Nose to Chin = ____.____cm

    J. Lips to Chin = ____.____cm

    K. Length of Lips = ____.____cm

    L. Tip of Nose to Lips = ____.____cm.

2. After you have measured these lengths, calculate the ratios indicated. (Remember **A/B** means **A** divided by **B** on your calculator.)

    A. A/G = _____

    B. B/D = _____

    C. I/J   = _____

    D. I/C   = _____

    E. E/L   = _____

    F. F/H   = _____

    G. K /E = _____

    Your answers to the above ratios should be near the Golden Ratio, 1.618. If you are very far off on any one of them, recheck both your measurements and your calculations.

3. Record the measurements of your face and then calculate each of the ratios for your face.

    A. Top of Head to Chin = ____.____cm

    B. Top of Head to Pupil = ____.____cm

    C. Pupil to Tip of Nose = ____.____cm

    D. Pupil to Lips = ____.____cm

    E. Width of Nose = ____.____cm

    F. Distance Between Outside Edges of Eyes = ____.____cm

    G. Width of Head = _____.____cm

    H. Hairline to Pupil = _____._____cm

    I. Tip of Nose to Chin = ____.____cm

    J. Lips to Chin = ____.____cm

    K. Length of Lips = ____.____cm

    L. Tip of Nose to Lips = ____.____cm

    A. A/G = _____

    B. B/D = _____

    C. I/J   = _____

    D. I/C   = _____

    E. E/L   = _____

    F. F/H   = _____

    G. K/E = _____

4. Would you say that your face is "classically Greek" (since classical Greek statues show all of these Golden Ratios)?

    _____

5. Record your mean average ratios, your group's mean average ratios, and your class' mean average ratio in the table below.

Ratio	Student Ratio	Your Groups' Average	G1	G2	G3	G4	G5	G6	G7	G8	Your Class' Average
A/G											
B/D											
I/J											
I/C											
E/L											
F/H											
K/E											
Column Average											

Teacher Notes

Activity 7

Go for the Gold

Math Strand

- ◆ Geometry and measurement
- ◆ Number sense
- ◆ Patterns and functions

Materials

- ◆ TI-73 calculator
- ◆ Ruler that measures to the nearest millimeter
- ◆ Transparency of Student, Group and Class Ratios Table (page 68)

The students will explore and use the concept of ratio in a real-world situation. They will make judgments regarding accuracy and precision of measurement.

Vocabulary

ratio	the comparison of two numbers by division
mean	a measure of central tendency (an average) that is calculated by taking the sum of the data set and dividing by the number of elements in the data set

Classroom management

1. Students should work in teams of four. Assign each group a number that will correspond to the G1, G2 (and so forth) names on the Student, Group, and Class Ratios Table.

2. This Class Project is a great example of statistics in action and of how scientific reports are created. Two scientific methods are used:

   a. First, a poll of statistics of each individual is taken. A group of individuals with a majority of statistics meeting a certain size criterion is searched for. This is a search for individuals of a certain *profile of characteristics.*

   b. A certain ratio (calculated body statistic) known throughout the group is averaged. Other ratios of the group are similarly averaged. Finally, these averages are evaluated to check for a maximum number that fall within a certain criterion. If a large majority do, we have a *trend.*

3. Another aspect of statistical thinking is the notion of a *sample.* It is known that in a *random* sample of about 30, if we take a characteristic and average it among the 30, there is a very high chance that this characteristic would average about the same in the same population from which the sample came. So, if the sample is large enough, you can make a statement about the "Classic Greekness," on the average, of all "typical students of that age."

Activity

Part 1

All measurements are done vertically or horizontally. Sample measurements are shown below. If students have difficulty determining where to measure, encourage them to use the lines at the side of the picture as guidelines.

A. Top of Head to Chin =   9.3 cm

B. Top of Head to Pupil = 4.6 cm

C. Pupil to Tip of Nose =   1.8 cm

D. Pupil to Lips =   2.8 cm

E. Width of Nose =   1.6 cm

F. Distance Between Outside Edges of Eyes = 4.4 cm

G. Width of Head =   5.6 cm

H. Hairline to Pupil =   2.7 cm

I. Tip of Nose to Chin =   2.9 cm

J. Lips to Chin =   1.9 cm

K. Length of Lips =   2.6 cm

L. Tip of Nose to Lips =   1.0 cm

Students will simply use the Home screen to calculate the ratios. First, set the MODE to 3 places (see screen at right).

Then, to calculate **A/G**, for example, press
[2nd] [QUIT] [CLEAR] 9 [.] 3 [÷] 5 [.] 6 [ENTER].

A. A/G = 1.661

B. B/D = 1.643

C. I/J = 1.526

D. I/C = 1.611

E. E/L = 1.600

F. F/H = 1.630

G. K/E = 1.625

Part 2

Again, students will use the Home screen to calculate the ratios.

Part 3

1. In column 2 (student ratio) of the table, students should record their ratios to three decimal places (to the nearest thousand).

2. In column 3 (your groups' average) of the table, students should record their group average ratios to three decimal places.

3. Students will provide you with their groups' average of each ratio. The results will be recorded on the Teacher transparency table. Students should record the group data on their table.

4. Name lists appropriately and enter the data as elements in the respective list. Use the table on the transparency (page 68) as a guide. To access lists, name lists, and use formulas in lists see Appendix A, B, and C, respectively. **RAT** will be a categorical list. Sample screens are shown below.

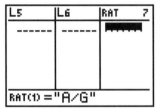 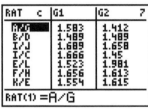

5. To find the average of the 8 different ratios, use the formula (where N = number of groups):   **AVE= (G1 + G2 + G3 + G4 ...GN)/N.**

    Sample screen shots are shown below.

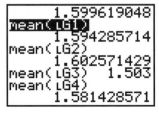

6. Find the mean average of each list and record on the table. Press [2nd][QUIT] [CLEAR] to clear the Home screen and then press [2nd] [STAT] [▶] [▶] [▼] [▼] (to select **mean**() [ENTER] (pastes command on the home screen) then [2nd] [STAT] and select the lists named **G1**, **G2** through **AVE**.

```
              1.599619048
mean( LG1)
              1.594285714
mean( LG2)
              1.602571429
mean( LG3)    1.503
mean( LG4)
              1.581428571
```
```
mean( LG4)
              1.581428571
mean( LG5)
              1.684285714
mean( LG6)
              1.632142857
mean( LAVE
              1.599619048
```

Wrap-Up/Assessments

1. Have students compare the averages if you average the last column and the last row on the teacher transparency.

2. Ask the students:

   ♦ *Are the averages the same?*

   ♦ *How "Greek" are the faces in your room?*

3. Have students write a paragraph answering the following question after thinking about it a few minutes or discussing it with others who have done the same work.

   ♦ *Why do you think the Greeks wanted to use the Golden Ratio to design the bodies and faces of statues for their gods and heroes?*

Teacher Transparency

RATIO	G1	G2	G3	G4	G5	G6	G7	G8	G9	AVE
A/G										
B/D										
I/J										
I/C										
E/L										
F/H										
K/E										
Avg										

Activity 8

Let's Do Summagic

In this activity you will:

♦ discover the magic (mathematics) in summagic
♦ use the distributive property

You will need to know this math vocabulary:

♦ distributive property
♦ greatest common factor
♦ coefficient
♦ like terms

Introduction

Have you ever seen anyone do mental math tricks quickly and wonder how they did it? In this activity, you will learn a trick that will involve adding a list of ten numbers in a split second.

The list is generated in a special way. Do you see a pattern?

2, 4, 6, 10, 16, 26, 42, 68, 110, 178

Problem

Listen as your teacher demonstrates the magic. Write the ten numbers of the class-generated list in Table 1 on the Student Worksheet, then find the sum.

Activity

Part 1

1. On the Home screen, find the sum of the ten numbers in Table 1 on the Student Worksheet and determine if your teacher was correct. (If you are not currently at the Home screen, press 2nd[QUIT] before you begin.)

2. Working with your teacher, complete Table 2 on the Student Worksheet. Use the two numbers 7 and 5 to numerically find the next eight terms.

Part 2

1. Listen as your teacher explains the process for determining the sum of a list.

2. Work with a partner to choose your own numbers and find the sum using the *summagic* rule.

3. Check your sum on the calculator using **sum(L2)**.

Activity 8

Let's Do Summagic

Record your results on the table below. Then answer the questions about the activity.

Table 1

1	2	3	4	5	6	7	8	9	10

Table 2

L1			L2
1			
2			
3			
4			
5			
6			
7			
8			
9			
10			

1. In Table 2 above, how many 7's are there?

   _____

2. How many 5's?

   _____

3. Write the mathematical expression as: ___ x 7 + ___ x 5

4. What factor do 55 and 88 have in common?

_____

_____

5. Rewrite the expression as: (11)(5)(7) + (11)(8)(5) = 11 (5 x 7 + 8 x 5).
Verify that the expression is the same as 55(7) + 88(5).
(Use your calculator to find the value of all three mathematical
expressions.)

_____

_____

_____

6. Is the expression 5(7) + 8 (5) in our numerically generated list? If so, what
number in the list?

_____

_____

Teacher Notes

Activity 8

Let's Do Summagic

Math Strand

- ◆ Algebraic reasoning
- ◆ Number sense

Materials

- ◆ TI-73 calculator
- ◆ Student Worksheet (page 71)

Students will discover the rule for the "summagic" problem by adding like terms and using the distributive property. They will use factoring to uncover the magic and explain the mathematics.

Vocabulary

Distributive property	For all real numbers a, b, c, a(b+c)= ab + bc
Greatest common factor	the greatest factor or divisor common to a set of 2 or more numbers
coefficient	the number in front of the variable; for example, in 7m, 7 is the coefficient
like terms	terms that contain the same variable(s) to the same power

Classroom Management

The majority of this activity is teacher-directed. The activity is divided into two parts. Part 1 could be used by itself for younger students. An abbreviated Part 1 along with Part 2 could be used for more experienced students.

Problem

Ask the students to explain how the numbers were generated in the opening paragraph. Draw a table on the board similar to the table in the opening problem. Select a student to randomly choose a one-digit number and write it as the first number in the table. Choose a second student to pick a second number and write it as the second number in the table. Magically, tell the class the sum by mentally multiplying the 7th number by 11. Have the students find the sum of the list of ten numbers on the Home screen to verify your answer.

Multiply by 11 Trick:

1. $32 \times 11 =$ 3   2

          $\wedge\wedge$

       3   5   2

2. $109 \times 11 =$ 1   0   9

           $\wedge\wedge\wedge$

        1   1   9   9

3. $67 \times 11 =$ 6   7

          $\wedge\wedge$

      6   13   7

    7   3   7

Activity

Part 1

1. For instructions on accessing lists, see Appendix A. Ask students to enter the numbers 1-10 as the first ten elements in **L1**. Choose a student to randomly pick a number and enter it as the first element in **L2**. (Any number will work, but you will probably want your students to choose numbers from 1-10.) Choose a second student to randomly pick a second number and enter it as the second element in **L2**.

a. Add the two numbers together and put the sum as element 3 of **L2**. Then add element 3 plus element 2 and put the sum as element 4. You can type the addition problem into an element: that is, to add 11 and 15, type **11 + 15** ENTER and the number **26** will appear as the next number in the list.

L1	L2	L3	2
1	7	------	
2	4		
3	11		
4	15		
5			
6			
7			

L2(5) =11+15

b. Continue **L2** by adding the previous two elements until you have filled in the tenth element.

L1	L2	L3	2
5	26		
6	41		
7	67		
8	108		
9	175		
10	283		

L2(11) =

2. You can now magically declare the sum of the ten numbers in **L2**. In the example above, the sum is 737.

a. To find the sum of **L2**, multiply the seventh element in **L2** by 11 quickly. An easy way to multiply by 11 is illustrated above.

b. You say "The sum of this list is _____. Let's check to see if this sum is correct." Go to the Home screen to find the sum of **L2**. Press [2nd] [STAT]▶▶ and select **7:sum(** [2nd][STAT] choose L2 [)] ENTER. Record the sum and verify that the sum is correct.

3. Ask, "How was I able to find the sum so quickly?"

  a. Give students a chance to explore **L2** and make conjectures. "Do you think I could do it again?"

  b. Have two other students choose two new numbers and repeat the process.

  c. After you have stunned your class by correctly finding the sum, develop the following on Table 2 to investigate the teacher's magic. Have the students complete Table 2 along with you. Use the two numbers 7 and 5 to numerically find the next eight terms. Ask, "What pattern can you see? Can we write these in a briefer form?" Help the students find the next two columns.

  d. After the table is completed, have the students answer the questions following the table.

L1			L2
1	7	=7	=7
2	5	=5	=5
3	7+5	=7 + 5	=12
4	(7+5) + 5	=7 + 2(5)	=17
5	(7+5+5) + (7+5)	=2(7) + 3(5)	=29
6	(7+5+5+7+5) + (7+5+5)	=3(7) + 5(5)	=46
7	etc.	=5(7) + 8(5)	=75
8		=8(7) + 13(5)	=121
9		=13(7) + 21(5)	=196
10		=21(7) + 34 (5)	=317

Answers to Student Worksheet

  1. 55

  2. 88

  3. <u>55</u> x 7 + <u>88</u> x 5

  4. 11

  5. See figure at the right.

  6. Yes, the 7th number.

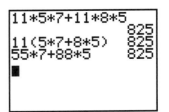

Extension

1. Develop the following list on the board.

1	a	=a
2	b	=b
3	b+a	=b+a
4	(b+a)+b	=a+2b
5	(b+a+b)+(b+a)	=2a+3b
6	(b+a+b+b+a)+(b+a+b)	=3a+5b
7	etc.	
8		
9		
10		

2. Ask the students:

   ♦ *How can we find the sum of list two in terms of a and b?*

   ♦ *How many a's are there? How many b's are there?*

   Find the sum of all ten elements in **L2** by combining the number of a's and number of b's to get the sum. (55a+88b)

3. Ask the students:

   ♦ *What do you notice about the numbers in front of the variables?*

   Lead the discussion to find that the numbers 55 and 88 are multiples of 11. Ask:

   ♦ *How could we write this expression in an equivalent form?*

   Using the distributive property the expression can be rewritten as: 55a+88b=11(5a)+11(8b)=11(5a+8b).

4. Ask the students:

   ♦ *Do you notice the expression 5a+8b in the list above?*
   (It is the seventh element in **L2**.)

   ♦ *How does the sum of the list compare to this term?*
   (It is eleven times the term.)

   Therefore, if you find the seventh element and multiply it by eleven you will have the sum of the list.

   ♦ *Will this work for other numbers?*

5. Have the students work in pairs to choose their own 2 numbers and repeat the activity. Ask them to find the sum using the summagic rule. Have them go to the Home screen and check their sum using sum (L2). Check with each of the pairs to see if they were able to find the correct sum.

6. To wrap up:

    a. Have a few of the groups explain to the class how they found their sum.

    b. Ask students to write the rule in their own words.

Going Further

1. Go to the Home screen. Clear the Home screen. Choose two numbers that you have found the sum for previously. For example, use 7 and 4. Let a=7 and b=4. Type [7] [STO▸] and press [2nd][TEXT], highlight **A**, [ENTER], use cursor to select **Done**, [ENTER]. Follow the same procedure to store 4 to **B**.

2. Using **A** and **B** on the Home screen, find the terms of the list as shown at the right.

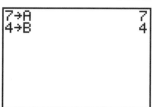

3. Discuss each line and compare the lines to the list of numbers previously generated on the board. Show that each algebraic expression gives the correct numerical value. Enter the sum as an algebraic expression **55A+88B**, then in the factored form of **11(5A+8B)**, (which is really 11 times the seventh term). Both expressions will display the same numerical value. Finally, multiply eleven by the seventh term demonstrating the "Summagic" rule.

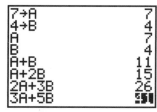

4. Have the students amaze a family member by finding the sum using the "Summagic" rule. Have them bring back a written note from the family member (or other suitable person) explaining how anyone, not knowing anything about how it works, could find the sum of the ten terms.

5. A famous mathematician, Leonardo de Pisa, better known as Fibonacci, investigated a sequence of numbers now known as the Fibonacci sequence: 1, 1, 2, 3, 5, 8, 13, 21, 35, …. Each number is the sum of the two previous numbers. This sequence is found in many places in nature, including pine cones, sunflowers, ridges on certain seashells. Also, when each number in the series is divided by the previous term, the results get

closer and closer to a value known as the golden ratio. Notice that the coefficients of **a** and **b** in the summagic rule are the numbers in the *Fibonacci* sequence. Have students research Fibonacci and the Fibonacci sequence and report their findings.

Activity 9

Taste Test

Objective

♦ To collect sample data and use the calculator to create pictographs, bar graphs, and pie graphs to demonstrate the favorite brand in the sample data

Materials

♦ TI-73 calculator

♦ Student Worksheet

In this activity you will:

♦ compare the tastes of different brands of cola, lemon-lime, and non-cola drinks

♦ find the class favorite in each category

♦ determine the favorite brand

You will need to know this math vocabulary:

♦ pictograph

♦ bar graph (single, double, and triple)

♦ scale

♦ axes

Introduction

What is your favorite soft drink? Do you prefer cola or lemon-lime drinks? If you prefer cola, do you have a certain brand that you like best? Can you tell the difference from one cola or another?

Problem

In this activity, you will taste three unlabeled brands of cola, lemon-lime, and non-cola drinks. You will then vote on only one of each brand. Water will be used between each taste test to clean your palate. If the prices of the three brands are the same and your class needs to determine which brand to sell at a school dance, the taste test will determine which brand the class should select.

Activity

1. Create four lists in the list editor named **BRAND**, **COLAS**, **LEMON**, and **NONCO**.

    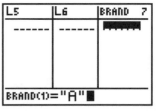

    a. Press LIST and use the ▸ key to move over to name the categorical list **BRAND**. (Remember to surround the first categorical list element with quotation marks.)

    b. Name the other three lists **COLAS** (the 3 brands of cola drinks), **LEMON** (the three brands of lemon-lime drinks), and **NONCO** (the 3 brands of non-cola drinks).

    c. Enter the appropriate data from the class data table.

    ✎ Answer question 1 on the Student Worksheet.

2. Set up the calculator to look at a **pictograph** of each of the three types.

    a. Turn off all statistical plots by pressing 2nd [PLOT] **4:PlotsOff** ENTER.

    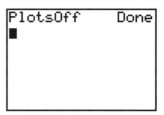

    b. Create a pictograph displaying your class' favorite cola drink. Display the Stat Plots menu by pressing 2nd [PLOT] ENTER.

    c. Define Plot 1 as shown in the screen at the right.

        Note: The calculator displays no more than seven pictograph icons. Therefore, if **Scale** is not big enough to cover the largest number in the list you get an **INVALID DIM** error.

3. Press GRAPH and TRACE.

    ✎ Answer questions 2 and 3 on the Student Worksheet.

4. Change the Plot 1 setup to display a **single bar graph**. Press GRAPH and TRACE.

    ✎ Answer questions 4 and 5 on the Student Worksheet.

5. Repeat the process with lemon-lime drinks on Plot 2 and non-cola drinks on Plot 3. Make sure you turn off the other two plots as you display each new graph.

✎ Answer questions 6 through 8 on the Student Worksheet.

6. Determine the overall favorite brand by summing the elements of Brands A, B, and C. Name a list **TOTAL** and then enter the formula as shown in the screen at the right.

7. Turn off all stat plots using [2nd] [PLOT] **4:PlotsOff** [ENTER]. Turn on Plot1 using **BRAND** as a categorical list and **TOTAL** as DataList1.

8. Press [GRAPH] and [TRACE].

✎ Answer question 9 on the Student Worksheet.

9. Go back to Plot1 and change it to a circle graph.

10. Press [GRAPH] and [TRACE].

✎ Answer question 10 on the Student Worksheet.

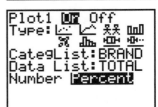

11. Finally, create a **triple bar graph** displaying all 3 brands with the 3 drink flavors. Use the setup shown at the right.

12. Press [GRAPH] and [TRACE].

✎ Answer questions 11 through 13 on the Student Worksheet.

Name _____

Date _____

Activity 9

Taste Test

Record your results in the tables below. Then answer the questions about the activity.

1. Take this Worksheet and a pencil to the taste test station. Please check only one drink in each brand category. You may not change your mind after you return to your desk. You do not need to fill out the student survey table or answer question 3 if you do not participate in the survey.

Student Survey Table

	Cola drink	Lemon-lime drink	Non-cola drink
Brand A			
Brand B			
Brand C			

2. Record the numbers preferred given to you by your teacher below in the Class Data Table.

Class Data Table

BRAND	Cola drink (COLAS)	Lemon-lime drink (LEMON)	Non-cola drink (NONCO)
Brand A			
Brand B			
Brand C			

3. Looking at the results of the table above, what brand do you think is Brand A? Brand B? Brand C?

    _____

4. Which cola brand was the class favorite?

    _____

5. What scale did you use when you set up your pictograph stat plot? Explain how you chose it.

    _____

    _____

    _____

6. How is the pictograph similar to the bar graph?

    _____

    _____

7. How is the pictograph different from the bar graph?

    _____

    _____

8. Which lemon-lime brand was the class favorite?

    _____

    _____

9. Which non-cola brand was the class favorite?

    _____

10. Was a certain brand consistently the favorite? Explain your reasoning.

    _____

    _____

    _____

11. Describe the results of the final **BRAND-TOTAL** single bar graph you displayed.

    _____

    _____

    _____

12. Describe what the circle or pie chart shows.

    _____

    _____

    _____

13. If you briefly explained to someone that the first set of three bars represents people who prefer Brand A, the middle set of three bars represent people who prefer Brand B, and the last set of three bars represent people who prefer Brand C, which brand do you think they would say is the most preferred? Explain.

_____

_____

_____

14. Sketch a triple bar graph below to show the results of the survey. Be sure to label and scale the vertical axes and make a legend to show the different brands.

Preferred Soft Drinks

| |
| |

colas   lemon-limes   non-colas

15. Based on the survey, which brand do you think should be sold at the school dance? Use the results of the survey and your reasoning to convince the class advisor on your recommended brand. You may use any of the graphs you feel would help in your recommendation.

_____

_____

_____

_____

Teacher Notes

Activity 9

Taste Test

Math Strand

♦ Statistics

Materials

♦ TI-73 calculator

♦ Student Worksheets (page 82)

♦ Teacher transparency (page 86)

♦ Soft drink samples

♦ 1 small paper cup per student (4-ounce sample cups work well)

♦ 12 large pitchers (plastic milk cartons could be used)

Students will use a sample to make a decision and use this sample and data analysis to make a convincing recommendation on the best brand to buy. They will use the calculator to create pictographs, bar graphs, and pie graphs.

Vocabulary

pictograph	a frequency graph where icons represent a certain frequency
bar graph	frequency are represented as either horizontal or vertical bars
scale	numbers used to represent the range or difference between the "tick marks" on graphs
axes	the horizontal or vertical reference lines used in graphs

Classroom Management

Setup

1. Have 12 containers to use for the 9 soft drink samples and 3 containers of water. Label the containers as Colas (Brands A, B, and C), Lemon-lime drinks (Brands A, B, and C) and Non-cola drinks (Brand A, B, and C). Lemon-lime drinks are drinks like Sprite®. Non-cola drinks are drinks like Dr. Pepper® or Mr. Pibb® You may choose to use two common brands such as Coke® and Pepsi® products and a third generic brand. (You could also use cookies, chips, or other food products that appear identical in place of soft drinks.) Use a clean table or flat desks to set up the survey stations for colas, lemon-lime drinks, and non-cola drinks.

2. A student should be assigned to each station to serve as the survey conductor. A second student may be used to keep a tally of participants' preferences. A frequency table should be prepared for each station so the station recorder can tally the results.

3. Tell the students the three brand types in advance without divulging which is Brand A, B, or C.

4. Students should have something to work on at their desks while the survey is being conducted. They should be asked whether they would like to participate in the survey since there may be a reason why they should not consume the products. If they do not want to participate in the survey, ask them to help collect the data in the survey.

5. It will take each student approximately 1 minute per station. They should probably have some resting or digesting time between stations. Describe to the students the process that will be used to send them to the 3 stations depending on your classroom setup. For example, Tables 1 and 2 may start at the cola station, tables 3 and 4 may start at the lemon-lime station, and tables 5 and 6 at the non-cola station. The survey conductors at each station will pour about 1 ounce of each brand in the cup and allow the participant to taste the product. Have the participant drink 1 ounce of water between brands to clean out the cups and their palates. The recorder should use the frequency table to tally the results. After all the students have taken the taste test, the results should be recorded on the Class Data Table Transparency below.

Class Data Table

BRAND	Cola drink (COLAS)	Lemon-lime drink (LEMON)	Non-cola drink (NONCO)
Brand A			
Brand B			
Brand C			

Activity

1. If students are not experienced in using and naming the lists you will need to walk them through it. Have them run the Setup editor before beginning their list. To do this, press [2nd][CATALOG] and scroll to **SetUpEditor,** then press [ENTER] [ENTER]. See Appendix A and B for additional instructions on accessing and naming lists.

2. When setting up any of the stat plots, you may need to show the students where to find the named lists. Press [2nd][STAT] and scroll down to find the appropriate list. (Press [ENTER] to select.) Another option is to use the Text editor and type in the name of the list. (See screen illustration at the right.) See Appendix D for instructions on setting up a stat plot.

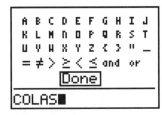

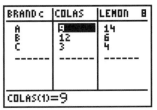

3. When setting up Stat Plot 1 as a pictograph, you may want to discuss how to determine the scale. One method would be to find the greatest number in the data list, divide it by 7, and round up to a whole number. Look at the data list named **COLAS**. Make sure the students understand that each icon represents the number used for the scale. Discuss what the fractional parts mean.

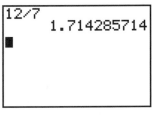

Answers to Student Worksheet

3. Answers will vary.

4. Answers will vary.

5. Answers will vary.

6. Sample answer- They both show frequencies.

7. Sample answer- In the pictograph, each icon represents a certain frequency number and there is no need for a vertical scale. In the bar graph, the height of the bar indicates the frequency number and the vertical scale is needed.

7. Answers will vary.

8. Answers will vary.

9. Answers will vary.

10. Answers will vary. This graph should be a good indicator of which brand to sell.

11. Answers will vary. It shows the percent of votes for each brand. This graph should also be a good indicator of which brand to sell.

12. Answers will vary.

13. Answers will vary. Students may need guidance on coming up with a legend and labeling and scaling the vertical axes depending on their graphing experience.

14. Answers will vary.

You may now want to disclose the name of each brand and answer the original question.

Going Further

You may have students investigate through the Internet or by some other means how manufacturers conduct taste tests and surveys. Possible questions for students to discuss in their portfolios:

♦ *What makes a good sample space?*

♦ *Describe a situation where consumers could be misled by statistics.*

♦ *Name other reasons for taking surveys besides selling consumers on certain products.*

EXPLORATIONS

Activity 10

Step Up

Objective

♦ To explore the concept of slope

Materials

♦ TI-73 calculator

♦ A ruler that measures in inches and centimeters

♦ String and tape

♦ Student Worksheet

In this activity you will:

- ♦ measure the vertical height (rise) and horizontal length (run) of a set of stairs

- ♦ find a ratio to describe how steep the stairs are

- ♦ create a graph to show the relationship

You will need to know this math vocabulary:

- ♦ ratio

- ♦ slope

- ♦ origin

- ♦ coefficient

- ♦ rise

- ♦ run

How steep are the stairs in your school? Are they all the same degree of steepness? Architects know that they cannot be too steep. They also know that if they are not steep enough they would be too long to fit in the space they need to. How can you numerically describe how steep something is like stairs, a mountain, or a ramp ?

Problem

In this activity, you will measure the height (rise) and depth (run) of stairs in centimeters and inches. Your teacher will tape a piece of string from the third stair to the bottom stair to represent the slope of the stairs. You will find the **ratio** of the vertical height (rise) to the horizontal height (run) or rise divided by run. This ratio is known as the **slope** of the line made by the string.

Activity

1. Type in the rise measurement in centimeters. Press [2nd] [CONVERT] and select **1:Length**, press [ENTER] and select **2:cm**, and then **4: inch**. You will use this to verify the accuracy of your measurements. Follow the same procedure with the run measurements.

   ✎ Record these measurements in Table 1 on the Student Worksheet.

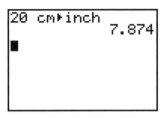

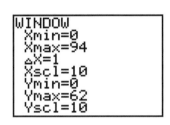

2. Use the Draw function of the calculator to draw a model of the stairs.

   a. Press [WINDOW] to set a friendly window as shown at the right. Make sure stat plots are off and there are no equations on in the [Y=] editor.

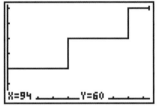

   b. Press [GRAPH] [DRAW] and select **8:Pen.** Use the cursor to move to the **origin** coordinates (0,0). Press [ENTER] to turn the pen on. Move the cursor up [▲] the vertical height of the stairs. To do this, press [▲] the number of times or the rise of the stairs. For example, if they are 20 cm tall, press [▲] 20 times. Then move the pen right [▶] the depth (horizontal length) of stairs. Continue this until you are about to leave the window. Do not go past your **Xmax** or **Ymax**. For example, in the screen shot at the right, do not go greater than **X=94** or **Y=62** or your window will change. Do this until you have at least 2 stairs. Press [ENTER] to turn the pen off.

3. Store your picture by pressing [DRAW] [◀] **1:StorePic** then **1** [ENTER]. If your stairs reappear, then the picture has been successfully stored.

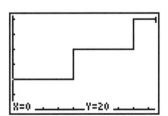

4. Use the Manual-Fit to place a line like the piece of string on your steps. On the Home screen, press 2nd [STAT] ◄ **3:Manual-Fit**, then 2nd [VARS] **2: Y-Vars** ENTER. Position the cursor at the top tip of stair 1. For example, at coordinates (0,20) in the screen shot shown in step 3 above. Press ENTER to set the endpoint of a segment that will contain the line that represents the string. Rise up the vertical height of the stairs (press ▲ the number of times of the height in cm) and run right the horizontal length (press ▶ the number of times of the depth in cm) until you arrive at the tip of stair 2. Repeat the process until you arrive at the tip of step 3.

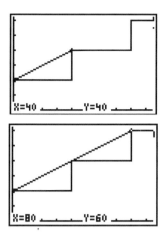

5. Press ENTER again. You should have an algebraic expression in the upper left corner of the screen. Press ENTER a third time to paste this expression into the Y= editor. Your stairs have disappeared and the string or line is all that is left.

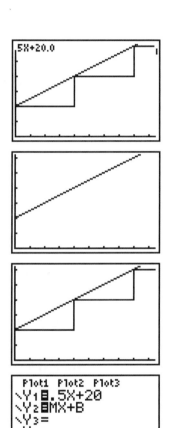

To recall your stairs, go to the Home screen and press DRAW ◄ **2:RecallPic** then **1** ENTER. Do this every time after you graph a line so you will have the string as your reference line. Remember to use the calculators scroll up and select feature to execute the command.

6. Look at the Y= editor and see the expression pasted on the right side of the equal sign. This is now an equation. In **Y2**, type the equation as shown at the right. In the example, **M= .5** and **B=20**.

✎ Answer questions 1 through 4 on the Student Worksheet.

7. Go to the Home screen and store the values you found for **M** and **B** to those variables as shown at the right. Make sure you use *your* values and not the example at the right. Then press GRAPH again and you should see the same line because **Y2** is on top of **Y1**. Use the Recall Picture command to get the stairs back.

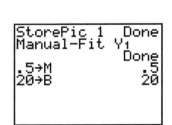

8. Go back to the Home screen and change the value of **B** to 0. To do this, use ▲ until you are on the command where you stored a value to **B**. Then press ENTER and edit it to change the value to 0.

9. Press GRAPH. Remember to recall picture 1 to get your stairs back.

    ✎ Answer question 5 on the Student Worksheet.

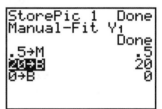

10. Now go back to the Home screen and change **B** back to the original value. Remember to use your scroll up and select feature to get the earlier command and don't forget to press ENTER to execute the command.

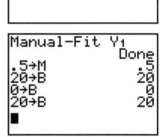

11. Change **M** to a greater decimal value. For example, add 0.25 to your original value of **M** and store the new value to **M**. Press GRAPH.

    ✎ Answer questions 7 through 8 on the Student Worksheet.

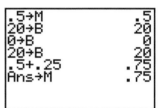

12. Change **M** to a smaller decimal value. For example, subtract .25 from your original value of **M** and store this value to **M**. Then press GRAPH.

    ✎ Answer questions 9 through 10 on the Student Worksheet.

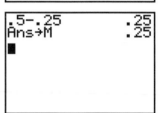

The number in front of the **X** is called a **coefficient**. In the equation **Y=.5X+20**, the coefficient of .5 is called the **slope**, and 20 is the **y-intercept**. (It tells where the line crosses the y axis.)

Y=MX + B is known as the **slope intercept form** of a linear equation where **M** is the slope and **B** is the y-intercept.

Recall the definition of slope from the beginning of this activity:

$$\text{Slope= } \mathbf{M} \qquad \mathbf{M} = \frac{\text{rise}}{\text{run}}$$

✎ Answer questions 11 and 12 on the Student Worksheet.

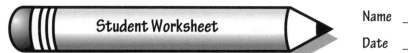
Activity 10

Step Up

Record your results on the table below. Then answer the questions about the activity.

Table 1

	Centimeters (to the nearest tenth)	Inches (to the nearest eighth of an inch)	convert cm to inches using convert function
Rise			
Run			

1. What was the rise of the stair you measured in centimeters?

   _____

   _____

2. What was the run of the stair you measured in centimeters?

   _____

   _____

3. Find the ratio of the rise to the run.

   _____

   _____

4. Record the values of M= _____ B= _____

5. Record the new value of B= _____ How does the slope of this new line compare to the slope of the stairs (the string)?

   _____

   _____

6. How are the lines different?

   _____

   _____

7. Record the new value of M= ____. How does the slope of this new line compare to the original line (the string)?

_____

_____

8. How are the lines the same?

_____

_____

9. Record the new value of M= ____. How does the slope of this new line compare to the original line (the string)?

_____

_____

10. Explain what you think the values of M and B stand for in the graphs of the equations Y=MX+B.

_____

_____

11. Calculate the slope ratio first using your centimeter measurements. Now calculate the slope ratio using your inches measurements.

_____

_____

12. How did the two ratios in question 11 compare?

_____

_____

Teacher Notes

Activity 10

Step Up

Materials

♦ TI-73 calculator

♦ Student Worksheets (page 93)

♦ A set of stairs with at least 3 stairs, or 6 congruent shoe boxes

♦ A ruler for each group with centimeters and inches

♦ String and tape

Students will use measurements on a real model to develop the concept of slope and linear functions. They will use the calculator to explore changing the slopes and Y intercepts in the slope intercept form of Y= MX+B.

Vocabulary

ratio	a comparison of two numbers by division
slope	the ratio of the rise to the run; the change in "y" divided by the change in "x"
origin	the coordinates (0,0) on a coordinate plane
coefficient	the number in front of the variable; for example, in 5A, "5" is the coefficient
rise	a vertical move on a coordinate plane that describes the change in "y" coordinates
run	a horizontal move on a coordinate plane that describe the change in "x" coordinates

Classroom Management

Students should work in small groups. When measuring the rise and run of the stairs make sure the groups can come to a consensus on a precise measurement. They should record the measurements in centimeters to the nearest tenth and inches to the nearest eighth of an inch. You should tape the string from the tip of the third stair to the tip of the first stair.

If stairs are not available, you could construct a model of stairs using six congruent shoe boxes arranged in three rows.

Activity

Depending on the calculator experience of your students, you may want to help with setup. Make sure that the stat plots are off and equations are cleared out of [Y=]. Press [MODE] and [2nd] [FORMAT] and use the setups shown at the right.

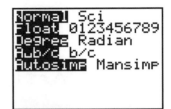

Sample data where **M** is the same and **B**=0

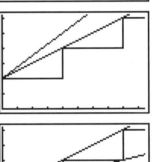

Sample data when **B** is the same and **M** increases and then decreases

Answers to Student Worksheet

1. Answers will vary.

2. Answers will vary.

3. Answers will vary.

4. Answers will vary.

5. Answers will vary. The slope of the new line is the same as the original line.

6. Answers will vary. The new line passes through the origin and the original line passes through higher up on the y-axis.

7. Answers will vary. The slope is steeper.

8. Answers will vary. They start at the same place or intersect the y-axis at the same place.

9. Answers will vary. The slope is not as steep.

10. Answers will vary. M is the ratio of the rise to the run also known as the slope and B is where the line intersects the y-axis.

11. Answers will vary but the slope ratios should be the same for centimeters and inches.

12. The ratio of the rise to the run should be very close to the same.

Going Further

♦ Have the students start at different locations on the y-axis and use the **Manual-Fit** function to create different lines.

♦ Explore lines with negative slopes.

EXPLORATIONS

Activity 11

Probably Not!

Objective

♦ To find the theoretical probability of different female/male combinations in a family of kittens

Materials

♦ TI-73 calculator

♦ Student Worksheet

In this activity you will:

♦ conduct an experiment to find the probability that all the kittens will be female

♦ determine the total number of possible female/male combinations in a five kitten family

♦ find the theoretical probability of different female/male combinations

You will need to know this math vocabulary:

♦ empirical probability

♦ theoretical probability

♦ combinations

♦ binomial outcome

Introduction

Mikel, a calico cat, is expecting kittens. Hillary, her owner, has five friends who want a calico kitten. However, calico coloring occurs only in female cats. If Mikel has five kittens, what is the probability that she will have exactly five female calico kittens?

Problem

You will work with your partner to *empirically* (experimentally) find the probability of Mikel, the cat, having a litter of five female kittens. You and your partner will flip a coin a total of 50 times where a head will represent a female and a tail will represent a male. Flipping a coin is one way of obtaining a *binomial outcome* (two equally likely outcomes). Then, you will determine all possible outcomes of kitten families and find out the probability of what should happen which is known as the *theoretical probability*.

Activity

1. The calculator can very quickly and quietly simulate the flipping of coins. You and your partner will use the coin toss function on the calculator to simulate tossing 5 coins 50 times. Clear the Home screen. (Press [2nd] [QUIT] [CLEAR]) Press [MATH] [▶] [▶] and select **6:coin(5** [)] [ENTER]. The number 1 will stand for a head (a female) and the number 0 will stand for a tail (a male). In the first screen at the right, the set of numbers {0 1 0 1 1} represents this order of female/male kitten births. {1st born-male, 2nd born-female, 3rd born-male, 4th born-female, 5th born-female} You will continue to press [ENTER] to flip the coins.

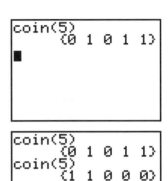

- ✎ Use the frequency table on the Student Worksheet to tally your results. You will take 25 trials while your partner tallies the results. Then you will change roles. Record a tally mark for each outcome. You should also record a tally mark in the last row of the table to help you keep track of the number of trials.

- ✎ After you and your partner have taken a total of 50 trials, record the totals on the table. Answer questions 1 through 3 on the Student Worksheet.

    Your teacher will record each group's results on the Class Data Transparency.

- ✎ Copy these results to the class data table and answer questions 4 through 6 on the Student Worksheet.

2. Next, enter this data into the calculator in the List editor. You will need to name three lists, **KITIS** (for kitties), **TFREQ** (for team frequency totals) and **CFREQ** (for class frequency totals). **KITIS** will be a categorical list that will include the following elements. Make sure you insert quotes around the first element **5F** to specify this list as the categorical list.

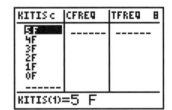

   a. Enter your data in the **TFREQ** list and the class data in the **CFREQ** list. You will now use these lists to create bar graphs.

   b. Turn off all stat plots ([2nd] [PLOT] **4:PlotsOff** [ENTER]).

   c. Display the stat plot menu ([2nd][PLOT]).

d. Define Plot 1 as a Bar graph, as shown at the right. Press [GRAPH] and [TRACE].

e. Turn off Plot 1 and define Plot 2 as shown in the second screen illustration at the right. Press [GRAPH] [TRACE].

✎ Answer question 7 on the Student Worksheet.

3. Make a list of all possible combinations of outcomes.

✎ Complete the summary table, keeping in mind that **MFFFF** and **FFFFM** are different outcomes where **MFFFF** means the first kitten born was a male and **FFFFM** means the last kitten born was a male.

✎ Complete Pascal's Triangle following the summary table and answer questions 8 and 9 on the Student Worksheet. Then use the summary table and Pascal's Triangle to complete the Theoretical Probability Table.

4. Name a new list **PROB** and enter the fractional probabilities from the Theoretical Probability Table. Use [b/c] to enter the fractions into the list.

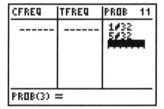

5. Name another new list **PRED** to predict the expected number of each family combination using the theoretical probabilities in **PROB** list. Use the total number of trials that the entire class collected from the class data table. You can take the number of teams times 50 trials per team or sum the list **CFREQ** by pressing [2nd] [STAT] [▶] [▶] **7:sum(** then [2nd] [STAT], scroll down to list named **CFREQ**, and press [ENTER][)][ENTER]. Use the sum in the formula shown at the right to make predictions.

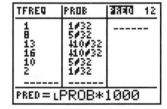

6. Create a double bar graph and compare the empirical and theoretical probabilities. Turn off Plot 1 and 2 and define Plot 3 as shown in the screen at the right. Press [GRAPH] [TRACE].

✎ Answer question 10 on the Student Worksheet.

Activity 11

Probably Not!

Record your results on the table below. Then answer the questions about the activity.

Coin toss simulation of Mikel's kittens

	Tally of Results	Total
5 Females		
4 Females		
3 Females		
2 Females		
1 Female		
0 Females		
trial tallies		

1. Which outcome(s) seem to be occurring the most often? Why do you think that is happening?

   _____

   _____

2. Which outcome(s) seem to be occurring the least often? Why do you think that is happening?

   _____

   _____

3. According to the experiment above, what is the probability that Mikel will have all female kittens?

   _____

   _____

Class Data Table

	T1	T2	T3	T4	T5	T6	T7	T8	T9	T10	T11	T12	T13	T14	T15	Total
5 F																
4 F																
3 F																
2 F																
1 F																
0 F																

4. Find the probability of Mikel having all female kittens using the class data.

_____

_____

5. How does this probability compare to the answer in question 3?

_____

_____

6. Which outcome(s) occurred the most using class data?

_____

_____

7. What do the bar graphs show? How are they similar? How are they different?

_____

_____

_____

Summary of Possible Kitten Family Combinations

5 Females ___outcome	4 Females ___outcomes	3 Females ___outcomes	2 Females ___outcomes	1 Female ___outcomes	0 Females ___outcome
FFFFF	MFFFF FMFFF FFMFF				

8.   How many different outcomes are shown in the table above?

_____

Pascal's Triangle

9. What can you observe about any similarities between the last row in Pascal's Triangle and the summary of outcomes in the Summary table?

_____

_____

Theoretical Probability Table

Kitten families	Probability as a fraction
5 females	
4 females	
3 females	
2 females	
1 female	
0 females	

10. Report on your observations of the two bar graphs. How are they similar?

_____

_____

_____

Teacher Notes

Activity 11

Probably Not!

Math Strand

- ◆ Probability
- ◆ Statistics

Materials

- ◆ TI-73 calculator
- ◆ Student Worksheets (page 102)
- ◆ Teacher transparency (page 110)

Students will investigate empirical and theoretical probabilities and make a connection to Pascal's triangle and binomial outcomes.

Vocabulary

empirical probability	the experimental probability of an event
theoretical probability	in theory, what should happen
combinations	an arrangement or listing where order is not important
binomial outcome	two events that are equally likely

Classroom Management:

Students should work in pairs. The class should be familiar with simple probability and should have been exposed to Pascal's Triangle. If they have not, you should introduce it as a special triangular arrangement of numbers with many interesting patterns. Complete the triangle with the students.

You may want to model tossing 5 different coins all together with each coin representing the sex of each kitten. Make sure they understand that a 5 female family means 0 male family.

Activity

1. In the eighth row on the Coin toss simulation of the table, the students can keep a trial tally record to keep track of how many trials they have taken. An optional method is using another calculator as an electronic tally. To do this, one student would use a calculator to toss the coin while the other student would use a different calculator to tally the results for the coin toss simulation. Have the students name a list on one of their calculators **Femal** for Females. The person operating this calculator will enter the number of females on each trial as an element of the list as the other student executes the coin toss command.

The screen shot at the right shows an example of the last three trials while the last three elements in the **FEMAL** list show the trials.

Students should sort the list by pressing [2nd][QUIT] to go to the Home screen and [2nd] [STAT] [▶] **2:SortD(** followed by [2nd] [STAT], selecting the list named **FEMAL,** and pressing [ )] [ENTER].

They should then scroll down the list and count the number of 5's, 4's, 3's, 2's, 1's and 0's and record the total on their frequency tables. They may switch calculators after the first 25 trials.

2. For more information about accessing lists, naming lists, and setting up stat plots, see Appendix A, B, or D.

Answers to Student Worksheet

1. 3 females and 2 females should be most likely but may not.

2. 5 females and 0 females should be the least likely but again they may not.

3. Answers will vary.

4. Answers will vary.

5. Answers will vary. However, the larger the sample space the closer the probability will be to the theoretical probability of 1/32.

6. Answers will vary. 2 or 3 females should occur the most.

7. Answers will vary. The middle bars representing 2 or 3 females should be the tallest and most likely to occur. The outer bars representing 0 or 5 females should be the shortest and the least likely to occur.

| 5 Females | 4 Females | 3 Females | 2 Females | 1 Female | 0 Females |
1 outcome	5 outcomes	10 outcomes	10 outcomes	5 outcomes	1 outcome
FFFFF	MFFFF	MMFFF	MMMFF	FMMMM	MMMMM
	FMFFF	MFMFF	MMFMF	MFMMM	
	FFMFF	MFFMF	MMFFM	MMFMM	
	FFFMF	MFFFM	MFMMF	MMMFM	
	FFFFM	FMMFF	MFMFM	MMMMF	
		FMFMF	MFFMM		
		FMFFM	FMMMF		
		FFMMF	FMMFM		
		FFMFM	FMFMM		
		FFFMM	FFMMM		

8.   32 outcomes

Pascal's Triangle

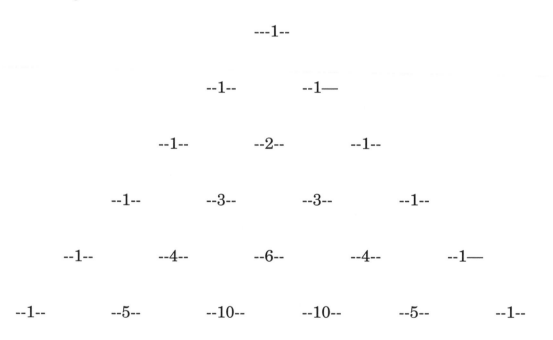

```
                        ---1--

                  --1--          --1—

              --1--      --2--      --1--

          --1--      --3--      --3--      --1--

      --1--      --4--      --6--      --4--      --1—

  --1--      --5--      --10--      --10--      --5--      --1--
```

9.   They are the same.

10.   The two bar graphs should be similar with the theoretical representation as perfectly symmetrical stairs up and back down.

Going Further

♦ Circle Graphs could be created using the empirical or theoretical data. The different combinations are presented in Pascal's triangle in an organized manner. The triangle could be extended with more investigations of probabilities of events with two equally likely outcomes.

♦ *Problem*: On a recent talk show a couple with 10 sons were the guests. Students could experimentally and theoretically explore this situation. They could also make predictions given certain criteria.

♦ *Connection to Science*: Investigate the genetic combinations of calico coloring. Calico coloring is a sex-linked color trait. Therefore, all calico cats that can reproduce are female.

Class Data Transparency

	T1	T2	T3	T4	T5	T6	T7	T8	T9	T10	T11	T12	T13	T14	T15	Total
5F																
4F																
3F																
2F																
1F																
0F																

Objective

♦ To investigate exponential growth in powers of 2

Activity 12

Materials

♦ TI-73 calculator

♦ Student Worksheet

A Penny Saved
is a Penny Earned

In this activity you will:

♦ calculate the amount of money an individual would receive using the doubling plan described below

♦ investigate patterns in powers of 2

You will need to know this math vocabulary:

♦ exponent

♦ power

♦ base

♦ factor

♦ exponential form

♦ scatterplot

Introduction

You may have heard of this age-old problem: A very wealthy family offered their son these choices if he agreed to do his daily chores for an entire month. These were his choices:

♦ *Plan A*: They would give him 1 penny the first day, 2 pennies the second day, 4 pennies the third day, 8 pennies the fourth day and continue doubling the previous day allowance until the end of the 31-day month.

♦ *Plan B*: Pay him a fixed amount of $1,000,000.

Which offer should he accept: Plan A or B?

Problem

In this activity, you will determine which offer will be more valuable by finding the difference in the two offers. You will investigate the graph of this model and some patterns involved.

Activity

1. To constantly double the previous amount, you can use the constant function of the calculator. Press [2nd] [SET] and use the setup shown at the right.

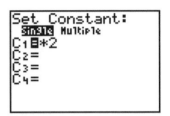

2. Press [2nd] [QUIT] [CLEAR] to go to the Home screen and clear it. Type [1] [CONST] and continue pressing [CONST] as the counter counts the number of times you multiply by 2.

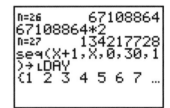

✎ Complete Table 1 and answer questions 1 through 4 on the Student Worksheet.

3. You may be familiar with expressing repeated multiplication by the same factor in exponential form. Recall that 2^5 is said to be in **exponential form** where 2 is the **base** and 5 is the **exponent.** The 5 tells how many times 2 is taken as a **factor.** Use your calculator to find the value of 2^5. Press [2] [^] [5] [ENTER].

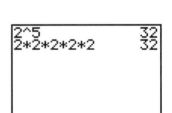

✎ Complete Table 2 on the Student Worksheet.

4. Use the list editor to investigate Plan A. Name a list **DAY** to represent the day number of the 31-day month.

  a. To save time in entering the numbers 1-31 in this list, you can use the **sequence** command. Press [2nd] [STAT] [▶] 7:seq(and then use the arguments shown in the screen at the right. Store this sequence to the list named **DAY**.

  b. Go to the list named **DAY** and you should have the numbers 1-31 entered as elements of this list. To the right of **DAY**, name two new lists **PPAID** (pennies paid), and **DPAID** (dollars paid). Instead of typing in each element you can write formulas to generate the lists. Study Table 2 and think of the list name **DAY** as variable **X** in the bottom row of Table 2. If you replaced **DAY** with **X**, what would the formula be to generate the **PPAID** (pennies paid) list? Discuss it with your group. Try it to see if it generates the correct values.

✎ Answer questions 5 and 6 on the Student Worksheet.

c. Now you will use the calculator to compute the cumulative total amounts after each day. Name 2 more new lists **CUMTP** (cumulative total in pennies) and **CUMTD** (cumulative total in dollars).

✎ Answer questions 7 through 11 on the Student Worksheet.

5. Define Plot 1 as a **scatterplot** by pressing [2nd] [PLOT] [ENTER] and define as shown in the illustration. Set up the following window to look at the first 10 days. Press [GRAPH] [TRACE]. Then adjust it to look at the first 15 days. Press [GRAPH] [TRACE]. Finally, adjust it to look at the first 30 days. Press [GRAPH] [TRACE].

a. To get a better idea of the shape of the graph, you can enter an equation into the [Y=] editor. If **X** = the day number and **Y** = the cumulative total amount paid in dollars, write an equation to describe this. Enter this equation into the [Y=] editor. **Y1**= (2^X - 1)/ 100. Press [GRAPH].

✎ Answer question 12 on the Student Worksheet.

b. Finally, create a graph of Plan B. Since it is a fixed $1,000,000, the equation is Y=1000000. Enter this equation in **Y2** . Press [GRAPH].

✎ Answer question 13 on the Student Worksheet.

c. Create graphs to investigate both plans. Press [2nd] [PLOT] **4:PlotsOff** [ENTER] to turn the plots off.

Name _____

Date _____

Activity 12

A Penny Saved is a Penny Earned

Record your results on the table below. Then answer the questions about the activity.

Table 1

	Day 1	Day 2	Day 3	Day 4	Day 5	Day 6	Day 7	Day 10	Day 20
N=									
amount earned in pennies	1	2	4						

1. How much will be earned in cents on the seventh day?

   _____

2. What is the **total** amount earned in cents and in dollars after 7 days?

   _____

3. How does the counter value (N) compare to the day number?

   _____

4. $1,000,000 = _____ pennies. Continue using constant key to determine the single day where Plan A will pay more than $1,000,000 in pennies. On what day will this occur? Record the amount in pennies and in dollars.

   _____

   _____

Table 2

Day	Pennies Paid	Power of 2	Cumulative total
1	1		1
2	2		1+2=3
3	4		1+2+4=7
4	8	2^3	7+8=15
5	16		31
6			
7			
10			
X			

5. If you replaced DAY with X, what would the formula be to generate the **PPAID** (pennies paid) list?

_____

_____

6. Write a formula to convert pennies paid to dollars paid in the **DPAID** list.

_____

7. Write a formula to express the cumulative total paid in pennies.

_____

8. Write a formula to express the cumulative total paid in dollars.

_____

9. Scroll down the **CUMTD** and find the total that would be paid at the end of the 31-day month. A second way to answer this question would be to sum the list named **DPAID**. (2nd [STAT] ▶ ▶ **7:sum(DPAID**) [ENTER])

_____

10. Scroll the list and find the day that plan A would exceed plan B.

_____

11. How much more money would be paid on Plan A than Plan B?

_____

_____

12. Describe the graph of Plan A.

_____

_____

_____

13. Describe the graph of Plan B.

_____

_____

_____

Teacher Notes

Activity 12

A Penny Saved is a Penny Earned

Math Strand

- ◆ Algebraic reasoning
- ◆ Number sense
- ◆ Statistics

Materials

- ◆ TI-73 calculators (one per pair or one for each student)
- ◆ Student Worksheets (page 114)

Students will explore exponential growth using powers of 2 and discover patterns in their sums.

Vocabulary

exponent	In a^b, b is the exponent and tells how many times a is used as a factor.
power	the exponent
base	In a^b, a is the base and is used as a factor b times.
factor	a number or variable to be multiplied
exponential form	written using exponents
scatterplot	a graph that shows the general relationship between two sets of data

Classroom Management

Students should work in teams of 2 to 4.

Activity

4. If students have limited background in using lists, you may need to lead this activity. For information about accessing lists, naming lists, and using formulas in lists, see Appendix A, B, and C respectively.

   a. If students are not familiar with using formulas in lists, you may want to lead the part of the activity where they are developing a formula to generate the pennies paid. Ask the students what they notice about the **DAY** number and the amount paid on that given day. The amount paid in pennies is a power of 2. *It is 2 to the power of the quantity of the day number minus one.*

Ask the students how they convert from pennies (cents) to dollars. *Take the PPAID list and divide by 100.*

DAY	PPAID	DPAID 9
1	1	------
2	2	
3	4	
4	8	
5	16	
6	32	
7	64	

DPAID = LPPAID/100

DAY	PPAID	DPAID 9
1	1	.01
2	2	.02
3	4	.04
4	8	.08
5	16	.16
6	32	.32
7	64	.64

DPAID(1)=.01

b. Next, the students will derive a formula to generate a cumulative total amount paid after each day. Note the pattern in Table 2. The cumulative sum is 1 less than a power of 2. *It is 2 to the power of the day number minus one.*

DPAID	SUMTP	CUMTD 10
.01	------	.01
.02		.03
.04		.07
.08		.15
.16		.31
.32		.63
.64		1.27

CUMTP =2^ LDAY−1

DPAID	CUMTP	SUMTD 11
.01	1	------
.02	3	
.04	7	
.08	15	
.16	31	
.32	63	
.64	127	

CUMTD = LCUMTP/100

DPAID	CUMTP	CUMTD 11
.01	1	.01
.02	3	.03
.04	7	.07
.08	15	.15
.16	31	.31
.32	63	.63
.64	127	1.27

CUMTD(1)=.01

c. Using the list to answer question 9 requires an understanding of scientific notation.

DPAID	CUMTP	CUMTD 11
167772	3.36E7	335544
335544	6.71E7	671089
671089	1.34E8	1.34E6
1.34E6	2.68E8	2.68E6
2.68E6	5.37E8	5.37E6
5.37E6	1.07E9	1.07E7
1.07E7	2.15E9	

CUMTD(31) =21474836...

sum(LDPAID)
        21474836.47

Answers to the Student Worksheet

	Day 1	Day 2	Day 3	Day 4	Day 5	Day 6	Day 7	Day 10	Day 20
N=		1	2	3	4	5	6	9	19
amount earned in pennies	1	2	4	8	16	32	64	512	524288

1. 64

2. 127, $1.27

3. It is one less. N-1 = Day

4. 100,000,000 pennies, Day 26; 134,217,728 pennies = $1,342,177.28

Table 2

Day	Pennies Paid	Power of 2	Cumulative total
1	1	2^0	1
2	2	2^1	1+2=3
3	4	2^2	1+2+4=7
4	8	2^3	7+8=15
5	16	2^4	31
6	32	2^5	63
7	64	2^6	127
10	512	2^9	255
X	2^(X-1)	2^(X-1)	2^X - 1

5. PPAID = 2^(**DAY** - 1)

6. DPAID = PPAID/100

7. CUMTP = 2^**DAY** -1

8. CUMTD = CUMTP/100

9. About 2.15×10^{7} or exactly \$21,474,836.47.

10. After 27 days, Plan A would exceed Plan B.

11. Plan A would pay \$20,474,836.47 more than Plan B.

12. Answers will vary. It is a curve that rapidly increases (increases exponentially).

13. Answers will vary. It is a straight horizontal line that remains constant at \$1,000,000.

Going Further

Look at other exponential growth or decay models using powers other than 2, such as world population.

Students can continuously fold a piece of paper in half.

♦ Analyze the layers-exponential growth.

♦ Analyze the regions-exponential growth.

♦ Analyze the areas of the regions - exponential decay.

Appendix A

Accessing Lists and Entering Data Into Lists

On the TI-73, a set of numerical or text data is called a list. The list editor is accessed by simply pressing $\boxed{\text{LIST}}$. There are 6 pre-named lists (**L1-L6**), but you can only see 3 at a time. For example, when you press $\boxed{\text{LIST}}$, you may get a screen similar to one of the following:

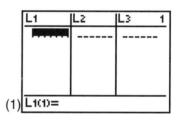

♦ In screen 1, the **1** in the upper right corner means the cursor is located in **L1**, more specifically as indicated at the bottom in the first space in the column named **L1**. At this position you can enter numerical (as real numbers) or text data. To enter the data, type the number or variable and press $\boxed{\text{ENTER}}$, which will take you down to the next position.

♦ In screen 2, the first element in **L3** is the number **2** and the **3** in the upper right corner means the cursor is located in **L3**.

♦ In screen 3, there are 2 named lists. The list named **COLOR** is called a *categorical* list since it contains the subscripted c after the name **COLOR**. The list named **CLASS** is a *data* list since there is not a subscripted c. The **8** indicates the cursor is in the 8th column of the list editor.

When graphing statistical plots, data lists are used for scatterplots, line graphs, histograms and both box plots. Categorical lists are used for bar graphs, circle graphs and pictographs.

♦ To define a list as a categorical list, enter the first element of the list in quotes as shown in screens 4 and 5. The remaining elements do not have to contain quotes. The quotation marks are found in the text editor by pressing [2nd][TEXT] and hard keys like the 5 can be used within the text editor.

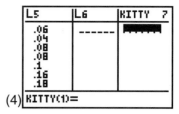

(4)

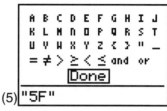

(5)

(6)

♦ To return the List editor to its original configuration (**L1-L6**), you may want to run the Setup Editor.

To do this, press [2nd] [CATALOG] (to access Catalog) as shown in screen 7.

(7)

To get to the **S**'s in the Catalog quicker, press [2nd][TEXT], select **S** (screen 8) and press [ENTER]. Scroll down to **SetUpEditor** (screen 9) and press [ENTER] to paste the command to the Home screen.

Press [ENTER] to execute the command (screen 10).

(8)

(9)

(10)

Appendix B

Naming Lists

There are 6 pre-named lists (**L1-L6**) that you cannot rename. You can delete them from the List editor but they are always retrievable.

1. For example, highlight **L2** as shown in screen 1.

2. Press DEL and **L2** will be deleted from the list editor (screen 2).

3. To retrieve **L2**, highlight the list you want to insert the named list **L2** in front of (screen 3).

4. Press 2nd [INS] (screen 4).

5. Press 2nd [STAT] **2** ENTER to rename the list (screen 5).

You can create a new list and name it anything you want. A list can be one to five characters long.

1. To do this, go right or left on the very top row to the first unnamed list (screen 6).

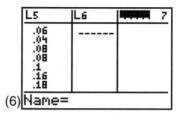

2. Use text, numbers, or a combination to create and name the list. The name will appear in the bottom row of the screen at the **Name** prompt (screen 7).

3. Press [ENTER] to place the name at the top of the list (screen 8). The cursor will move to the first position in the list.

If the SetUpEditor is executed or the list is deleted, it will still be retrievable. You can insert it between two lists, or you can go right or left until you get to the first unnamed list position.

1. Place the cursor where you want to insert the list.

2. To retrieve the list, press [2nd] [STAT] and use the cursor to move down or up to the name of the list you are retrieving.

3. Select it and then press [ENTER] to paste in on top of the column. Press [ENTER] again.

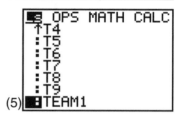

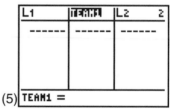

Appendix C

Using Formulas
in Lists

1. To use a formula in a list:

a. Highlight the name of the list you want to assign the formula to. You must be at the very top of the column or you will get an **ERR:DATA TYPE** message.

L1	L2	▮	3
1	1	------	
1	2		
2	3		
3	5		
5	8		
8	13		
13	21		
L3 =			

Correct Cursor Position

L1	L2	L3	3
1	1	▮▮▮▮	
1	2		
2	3		
3	5		
5	8		
8	13		
13	21		
L3(1) =			

Incorrect Cursor Position

b. Use any operations or calculator functions with real numbers and previously defined lists. If **L3=L2/L1**, for example, press 2nd [STAT] and retrieve **L2** by pressing **2** ÷, then 2nd [STAT] **1** ENTER.

Note: If you select a named list by pressing ▾ or ▴ to move up or down, you will have to press ENTER twice.

L1	L2	▮	3
1	1	------	
1	2		
2	3		
3	5		
5	8		
8	13		
13	21		
L3 =L2/L1			

L1	L2	L3	3
1	1	1	
1	2	2	
2	3	1.5	
3	5	1.6667	
5	8	1.6	
8	13	1.625	
13	21	1.6154	
L3(1) =1			

2. You can use a formula like a formula in a
spreadsheet by inserting the formula in quotation
marks.

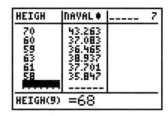

♦ When you enter new numbers in the
independent list, the dependent list with the
formula assigned to it does the calculation. In
the screen at the right, **HEIGH** is independent,
whereas **NAVAL** is dependent.

♦ Another difference you will notice when you
enclose formulas in quotes is that when you go
back to the top of the list, the formula will
appear in the **Name** field instead of the data in
set notation.

Formula with quotes

Formula without quotes

A very common error that occurs when using formulas
is the **DIM MISMATCH** error, which means the lists
being used in the formula do not have the same
number of elements.

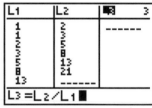

1. To correct this problem, go to the List editor, press
CLEAR, and scroll down the lists used in the
formula.

2. Either add or delete elements to make the lists
contain the same number of elements.

EXPLORATIONS

Appendix D

Setting Up
Statistical Plots

Statistical plots (stat plots) are graphical representations of data that has been stored in lists.

1. Make sure you have entered the data into the lists.

2. Make sure you have turned off any equations in $Y=$ editor or cleared them out unless you want to graph them with your stat plot. Press $Y=$ to check this out. This screen will also tell you if any of the three plots are on.

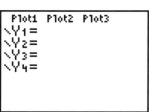

**All plots off
and nothing in Y=**

   a. To turn off Plots 1 and 3 move your cursor up to the top row on Plot 1, then press ENTER. Do the same with Plot 3.

   b. To turn off **Y2**, move your cursor to the = sign and press ENTER.

**Plots 1 and 3 ON and
equations in Y1 and Y2**

3. Set up the statistical plot by pressing 2nd [PLOT].

   a. Decide which plot you want to turn on and press that number. The cursor will be blinking on **ON**.

   b. Press ENTER.

   c. Press ⏷ to move down to **Type**.

   d. Use ▶ to move to the type you prefer and then press ENTER.
   Options:

⸛⸱**Scatterplot**	⌇⌃**Line graph**	⁑⁑**Pictograph**	▥▥**Bar Graph**
⊛**Pie chart**	⊞ⅲ**Histogram**	⊡⋯**Box Plot**	⊡⊡ **Modified Box Plot**

4. Define the **Xlist** and **Ylist** for 2-variable statistics as in Scatterplots and Line graphs. To access the named lists press [2nd][STAT], make your selection, and press [ENTER]. Categorical lists must be used for Pictographs, Bar Graphs and Pie Charts. The categorical named lists are found in the same location as the other lists ([2nd][STAT]). Follow the directions in the activity to set up or define the plot.

5. Set the [WINDOW] according to the activity instructions or press [ZOOM] **7:ZoomStat** to have the calculator set the window.

6. [GRAPH] the statistical plot.

Appendix E

Linking

Linking two calculators

You can transfer data from one TI-73 to another using the unit-to-unit cable.

To connect the TI–73 to another device using the unit-to-unit cable, use the link port located at the center of the bottom edge of the calculator.

1. Insert either end of the unit-to-unit cable into the TI–73 port very **firmly**.

2. Insert the other end of the cable into the port of the other device.

Next, set up the TI–73 to receive data:

1. Press APPS to display the **APPLICATIONS** menu.

2. Select **1:Link** and press ▶ to display the **Link RECEIVE** menu.

3. Select **1:Receive**. The message **Waiting...** and the busy indicator are displayed. The receiving unit is ready to receive transmitted items.

   To exit the receive mode without receiving items, press ON, and then select **1:Quit** from the **Error in Xmit** menu.

To select data items to send from the sending unit to another calculator, follow these steps:

1. Press APPS to display the **APPLICATIONS** menu.

2. Select **1:Link** to display the **Link SEND** menu.

3. Select the type of data you want to send. The corresponding **SELECT** screen is displayed. Each **SELECT** screen, except the one for **All+**, is displayed initially with no data items selected.

4. Press ▲ and ▼ to move the selection cursor (▶) to an item you want to select or deselect.

5. Press ENTER to select or deselect an item. Selected names are marked with a black box (■). To exit a **SELECT** screen without transmitting any items, press 2nd [QUIT].

6. Repeat steps 4 and 5 to select or deselect additional items.

7. Press ▶ to select **TRANSMIT**.

8. Press ENTER.

When transmission is complete, the receiving unit will still be in the receive mode. Press 2nd [QUIT] to exit the receive mode.

Linking a calculator and a computer

TI-GRAPH LINK™ allows you to transfer information from the TI-73 to a computer or from a computer to a TI-73. The software comes in Windows and Mac versions.

To use TI-GRAPH LINK:

1. Connect the TI-GRAPH LINK cable to an open port on the back of your computer. You will need to know the name of this port (for example, COM1) for the software configuration.

2. Start the program and connect the calculator to the cable through the link port on the bottom. When transferring files (programs, lists, and so forth) from the TI-73 using the TI-GRAPH LINK, the calculator should be turned on and at the Home Screen. If you place the calculator in the Link application, you will get an error. When collecting screen images from the TI-73, most of the time you can be anywhere you wish.

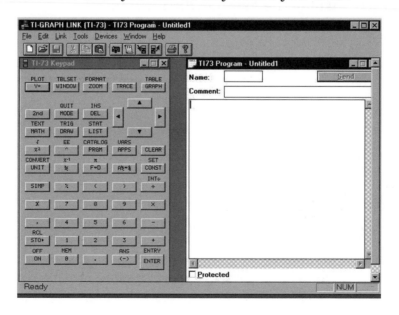

The initial screen has several icons to execute common tasks. These include:

Capturing the screen displayed on the TI-73

Sending files to the TI-73

Receiving files from the TI-73

3. To use any of the options, click on the appropriate icon or select the option from the **Link** menu.

    a. To capture a screen, once you have the image that you want on the screen of the TI-73, click **Get Screen**. Then click the appropriate option and repeat the **Get Screen** option for another image from the TI-73, or select **Done**.

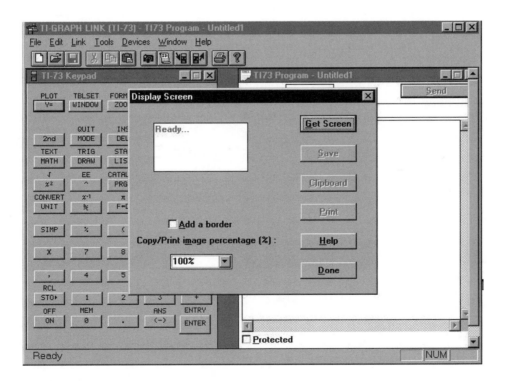

b. To transfer files from the computer to the TI-73, press the appropriate icon and select the files needed to send to the TI-73.

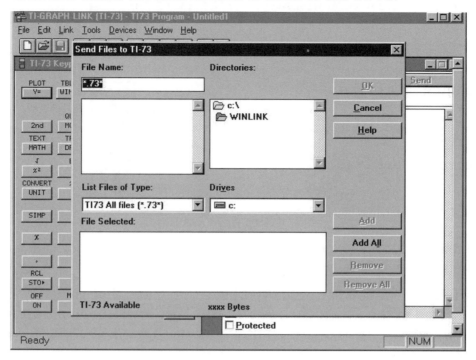

c. To transfer files from the TI-73 to the computer, select the appropriate icon and then select (by double-clicking) the files to transfer and then click on **OK**. Make sure you note the directory in which you placed the files. Note also that you can group files if needed.

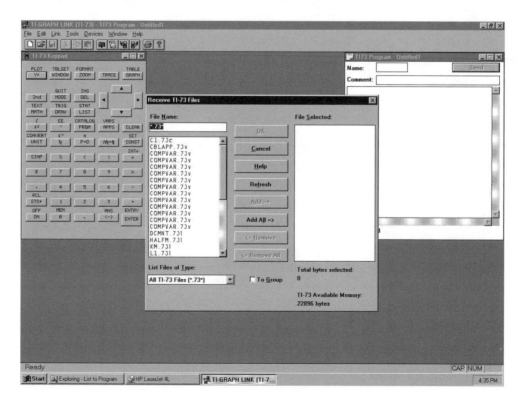

Index